"What Are You

"Make ____
sudden ____
live ag ____ a
few lessons? I shan't let you lose what life and
love can give!"

"Love?" Clare shook her head. "I shall never
fall in love! You know why—so stop torturing
me! Let me go—"

"Your body's made for pleasure—a man's
pleasure as well as your own—"

"Stop it!" Tears rolled unchecked down her
cheeks, but he was immune to them. "You're
a beast! I shall tell my brother what you've
done to me!"

"I don't think so," he disputed imperturbably.
"This, Clare, is between you and me."

ANNE HAMPSON
has the same impetuous streak as her
heroines. It often lands her in the middle of a
new country, a new adventure—and a new
book. Her first-hand knowledge of her
settings and her lively characters have
combined to delight her readers throughout
the world.

Dear Reader:

Silhouette Romances is an exciting new publishing venture. We will be presenting the very finest writers of contemporary romantic fiction as well as outstanding new talent in this field. It is our hope that our stories, our heroes and our heroines will give you, the reader, all you want from romantic fiction.

Also, *you* play an important part in our future plans for Silhouette Romances. We welcome any suggestions or comments on our books and I invite you to write to us at the address below.

So, enjoy this book and all the wonderful romances from Silhouette. They're for *you!*

Karen Solem
Editor-in-Chief
Silhouette Books
P. O. Box 769
New York, N.Y. 10019

ANNE HAMPSON
Second Tomorrow

Silhouette Romance

Published by Silhouette Books New York

SILHOUETTE BOOKS, a Simon & Schuster Division of
GULF & WESTERN CORPORATION
1230 Avenue of the Americas, New York, N.Y. 10020

ISBN: 0-671-57016-1

First Silhouette printing July, 1980

10 9 8 7 6 5 4 3 2 1

Second Tomorrow

Chapter One

Clare Winter stood on the verandah of her bedroom and gazed across the tropical gardens to the sea, its colour in the late afternoon sun a kaleidoscope of blues and emeralds and yellows. Beyond the lagoon and coral reef other Out Islands lay strung over the face of the Atlantic just across the Gulf Stream from Florida. Flamingo Cay, a little world of its own no more than three and a half miles long, was on the Tropic of Cancer, and it was to this lush green island that Clare had come just over a month ago at the invitation of her brother, Phil, who had been manager of the island's one hotel, the Rusty Pelican, for the past two years.

'Go, my love,' Clare's mother had urged. 'The change will do you good.'

What her mother really meant was that the change might help her daughter forget the tragedy that had been with her for almost five years, the tragedy that had occurred only a week before the day fixed for the wedding.

Five years. . . . Clare was no nearer forgetting that fateful day when her future brother-in-law had come to her home and asked for her father. Her fiancé, Frank, twenty-six and already a deputy-head at the school where he taught, had been taken ill at work and died in the ambulance on his way to the hospital. No one knew he had a heart complaint; he did not know himself, simply because the attack that killed him was the first he had had.

Clare had never looked at another man since, and she intended to remain a spinster, cherishing Frank's memory until the day she died. She had no desire to forget, so why had she allowed her mother to persuade her to come here and take up the post of secretary-receptionist which Phil had offered her? He had written to their mother saying that Sally, the girl holding the post, was getting married and leaving the island, so the post would be vacant.

A small sigh escaped Clare as she turned, entering her bedroom. She ought not to have come. Every Saturday she had visited Frank's grave, meeting his mother there and together they would put their flowers into the vases they had emptied and cleaned out. Mrs Weedall, a thin greying little woman who looked ten years older than her fifty-two years, would talk about her son, and she and Clare would attempt to comfort one another, but invariably one or both would leave the cemetery in tears. Clare's mother would be furious, while her father would sit and brood and wish he were young enough to risk throwing up his job so that they could move to another district, away from the cemetery and the woman who was always reminding Clare that Frank had worshipped her and, had the positions been reversed, would have remained true to her memory forever.

'That woman's a blight on our daughter's life!' Clare had once heard her father exclaim. 'I wish to God we could get her away—a thousand miles away!'

Well, she was a lot more than a thousand miles away, mused Clare, absently taking up a comb from the dressing-table. Although she had agreed to come here, giving up an excellent post to do so, she had no intention of allowing Frank's image to fade from her memory. It was a lonely path she had chosen but one she meant to follow to the very end. She had known that her parents' belief was that, if only she could get away from Mrs Weedall's influence, she might find someone else and fall in love again. Nothing could be more remote than that possibility. . . .

It was at this juncture in her mind-wanderings that the strong stern face of Luke Mortimer intruded and she frowned as she began to take the comb through her honey-brown hair. Her hazel eyes were darkened as they stared back at her through the gilt-framed

mirror. Luke Mortimer, friend of her brother,
realtor from Miami who had bought some
land on Flamingo Cay. . . . Clare determinedly
erased his picture from her thoughts, drawing
the comb again through her silken hair. Her
face was pale, her skin like alabaster, its texture
so fine that tiny blue veins were revealed by its
transparency at her temples. Her forehead was
clear and wide above delicately-arched brows;
her cheekbones were high, and a little too
prominent for real beauty. But there was a
wealth of character in her features, an abundance of compassion in the wide, generous
mouth. Her chin was firm and pointed, her neck
long and smooth above gracefully-sloping shoulders. Of medium height, she had a figure that
Frank had proclaimed to be perfect. And he
should know, his mother had said, because his
post was that of athletics instructor.

Putting down the comb, Clare turned once
again, stepping through the window onto the
verandah. She was restless, undecided about
staying. . . . She was always restless and undecided whenever she allowed Luke Mortimer's
disturbing image to superimpose itself upon her
memories.

The Tavern Restaurant at the Rusty Pelican
had a distinctly nautical flavour, its decor in-
cluding an assortment of rudders, props, ships'
wheels and anchors, heavy ropes knotted into
fantastic and intricate designs and shapes. Vari-

ous and unusual ships' lamps added their light to that given off by the candles on the tables, and on one wall was a large mural of the Out Island Regatta.

Clare always had the evening off and tonight, as usual, she took her place at a table by the window that overlooked the marina. Graceful yachts tugged gently at their moorings; smaller motor-craft and fishing-boats littered the water-front, while on the purple horizon a cruise liner lay silhouetted against the star-spangled dome of the sky. Clare was expecting to be joined by her brother, who usually dined around half-past eight or a quarter to nine. He arrived at length but instead of sitting down he leant over her shoulder and said, 'Luke's dining here with us, Clare, but we're having a drink first in the lounge.' His hand came beneath her elbow and she rose, automatically and at the same time reluctantly. She had no wish to spend the next couple of hours in Luke Mortimer's company. But of course she could not voice her objection and she allowed herself to be ushered into the lounge and along to a table screened by a profusion of exotic plants in urns and other attractive containers.

Luke rose and swept a glance from her head to her feet before saying, 'Good evening, Clare. Had a good day?'

She nodded and sat down. 'Yes, thank you, Luke. Have you?'

'Every day's a good day.' One corner of his

mouth lifted in a sardonic smile. 'Each new day is what you make it—' He paused in thought. 'Perhaps I should have said that each day is what you *intend* to make it.'

Clare set her teeth. Phil, alive to the situation that had been gradually developing between these two, diplomatically broke in to ask what they were drinking.

A few minutes later they were sipping well-mixed cocktails while they listened to the discourse going on around them. The history of the Out Islands was being talked about by one small group somewhere on their right, while another little company were arguing the best method of catching certain fish. A doctor from Miami was discussing rare seashells with the blonde in room twenty-nine, and Jim Dawson, a local, was expounding on the prospects of the crawfish season. Fish of incredible variety abounded in these tropical waters and inevitably they were a fisherman's paradise. Half the fish eaten in the restaurant this evening would have been caught earlier in the day by the guests themselves.

'Sir. . . .' The soft respectful voice of one of the waiters broke into something Phil was about to say. 'Mr Renshaw's complaining again. . . .'

An impatient sigh from Phil before he spoke. 'I'll come along. He asked to see me, of course?'

'Yes, sir. It's the Steak Bordelaise this time. He's insisting that it isn't cooked correctly.'

Phil rose, excused himself and went off. Clare and Luke exchanged glances before their eyes followed the figure of Phil as he threaded his way between the tables, making for the high arched doorway leading into the restaurant.

'Not an easy job, that of hotel manager,' observed Luke, reaching forward to take up his glass.

'Phil likes it all the same. You don't get many like Mr Renshaw. He'll be leaving on Thursday and we shall all be happy again.'

'Happy?' Again that sardonic lift of his mouth at one corner.

Clare said quietly, 'My brother had no right to tell you so much about me.'

'Don't blame him altogether. When he said you were coming here to take up the post in the hotel I naturally showed a little interest, and asked if there was any special reason for your coming out here to him. As you're aware, we haven't known each other long and he'd never said much about his background, so I thought that perhaps you were alone in England, that you had no parents.'

Clare nodded absently. Phil had told her how he came to know Luke. It was just over a year ago, when the land was up for sale. Luke came over and stayed at the Rusty Pelican while he negotiated with the owner of the land. After making the purchase Luke then returned to his home in Miami Beach where he had an architect plan a house for him, and others which he intended to sell. He returned to Flamingo Cay several times to supervise the building of his house, and had moved in about two months ago. Clare had deplored the idea of the building programme, feeling that it was people like Luke who spoiled the beautiful islands of the world by their greed for money.

'A man of thirty-five can't retire,' said Phil reasonably when, on learning that Luke was already a millionaire, she had said he ought to give up trying to increase his wealth. 'His business is building,' Phil had added, 'and you can be sure that what he builds here will enhance rather than detract from the beauty you see around you.'

Undoubtedly the house already built was beautiful. Silver Springs, Luke had called it, because of the two natural springs that cascaded down the coral rocks that rose to one side of the grounds. An avenue of stately Royal Palms happened to have been conveniently placed to form a drive leading to a magnificent site where the lovely villa had been constructed around a courtyard of coral rock which dripped with exotic flowers—orchids, flame vines, ixora and hibiscus blossoms exploding in the lacy shade provided by the casuarinas and palms which were well established long before the land was up for sale. Tastefully landscaped gardens and manicured lawns surrounded the villa which had its own private beach of talcum-soft pink sand. Idyllic was the only description Clare could give to the house when, a week after her arrival at Flamingo Cay, she had been invited, with her brother, to a buffet party given to a few friends by Luke.

Suddenly, a little movement brought Clare

back to the present and she looked at her companion.

'Phil told you that I had been engaged, and that my fiancé had died a week before the wedding.' A statement but she expected an answer.

'Yes, he did,' A slight pause ensued and then, pointedly, 'It's five years ago, Phil said.'

'That's right.' Absently, she handled her glass but made no attempt to take it up. The chatter going on all around her could still be heard, and above it the strains of Bahamian music being softly relayed by a tape recorder.

'It's time you were picking up again.' The bluntness of the words caused Clare to give a start. He had no right to adopt such a familiar attitude—and, in fact, for the first three weeks he had practically ignored her, speaking coolly if they should happen to meet, and more often than not looking through her rather than at her. But about a week ago he had changed in some subtle and yet dramatic way, beginning to take more interest in her than was necessary, and certainly more than she desired! 'Aren't you settled?' asked Luke when she did not speak.

'Here, you mean? In my job?'

'That's right. I've the impression that you don't want to stay.'

Again she gave a start, his perception amazing her.

'It's true that I'm unsettled,' she told him frankly after a pause. 'I often feel I should never have come.'

'Phil said you'd given up a good post to come here.' There was a coldness in his voice now that was almost callous. He had no heart, she thought, no sensitivity to the loss she had sustained. He was unemotionally looking in from the outside, perceiving a situation which he regarded as stupid—that of a girl who was caught up in a sorrow which she could quite easily have thrown off. She glanced at him as he idly began to peruse the menu that had just been handed to him, noting the fine, aristocratic lines of his sun-bronzed features. He leant back in his chair, and to Clare there was a certain arrogance even in the posture he assumed; he was lounging comfortably, and yet his head was held upright, set on broad, immaculately-clad shoulders. His face was half-turned towards her, its finely-chiselled lines and contours sharply silhouetted even though the light all around was muted. The very dark brown hair, the faint arch of the brows, the flexed set of the mouth and jaw, the steely glints in eyes that could be grey but often seemed almost black . . . all these combined to give an impression of pride and power and great strength of character. An unusually arresting and handsome man, Clare was admitting, but a formidable one for all that. Phil had said his attitude towards women was cynical; he treated them as inferiors, regarded their fight for equality with something akin to contempt.

She said, still watching his face intently as he read the menu, 'Yes, I did give up my job,' but she immediately added that she would have little difficulty in obtaining another.

'You'd better stay.' Authority in his voice and a challenge in his stare as he regarded her over the top of the menu. Clare lifted her chin at his tone, her eyes glinting.

'I shall do what suits me,' she returned with a trace of defiance which, she thought, ought not to have been necessary.

'I expect you shall,' was his terse rejoinder as he glanced at the tilted chin, 'regardless of whether or not it suits others.'

She frowned in puzzlement. 'Others? My brother—and who else?'

'Your parents. They're exceedingly troubled about you.'

'Phil told you far too much,' she said tautly.

'As I've said, I was curious as to why you should be taking the post here. Phil told me a few things. It wasn't much.'

'But enough to make you decide on giving me advice.'

He shook his head impatiently. Ignoring her words he said, looking directly at her, 'Has it never occurred to you that your attitude is selfish?'

'No,' she flashed, colouring with indignation, 'it hasn't!'

'Then you should think a little more deeply about it,' he recommended. 'From what Phil told me your father and mother are very unhappy people.'

She frowned and bit her lip. What he said was

true, of course, but never had she stopped to
think that there might be selfishness in her
wanting to keep Frank's memory green. Luke's
accusation troubled her, going deeper than was
comfortable. Anger against him rose swiftly,
anger that he should concern himself with what
was not his business.

However, she had no time to say anything, for
her brother came back and soon they were in the
restaurant, sitting at the table by the window,
Luke's whole attention on the boats moored in
the marina. Phil looked at his sister and smiles
were exchanged. She was proud of him, always
had been. Tall and slim and good-looking in a
gentle, refined sort of way, he seemed all wrong
as a bachelor because undoubtedly he would
make a wonderful husband. But he had concen-
trated on his career, his ambition being to
become manager of an hotel. He was making a
great success of it and already there had been
hints from his superiors that he would be given
the management of a luxury hotel that was to be
built on one of the larger islands of the Bahama
group.

Luke turned presently and remarked on some
of the yachts, mentioning their owners. Everyone here seemed to own a yacht, mused Clare,
thinking of the beautiful vessel belonging to
Luke which was moored at his private jetty
down-beach from his house.

The starters came and when they were eaten
Phil and Clare got up to dance, the calypso

music being played by a native combo occupying a flower-bedecked platform at one end of the room. She was suddenly acutely conscious of Luke's eyes following her. She saw them slide from her face to her figure—to her tiny waist where the turquoise-blue dress she wore fitted snugly before flowing out in an abundance of subtle folds that swayed as she danced. Something stirred within her . . . something she had known before and which angered her. That Luke's presence and his interest should disturb the serenity of her mind was bad enough; but in addition he had the ability to superimpose his own image upon that of her dead fiancé, almost blotting out the picture she was ever striving to keep before her. She had considered herself immune to the attractions of any man, but she was having to admit that those of Luke Mortimer affected her in a way which created a deep and totally illogical resentment towards him.

She and her brother returned to the table for the second course. Phil had ordered turtle steak, and Clare grouper cutlets and a salad, while Luke was having a lobster ragout in the shell 'Newburgh.' When the meal was over Luke asked Clare to dance and she rose hesitantly, doubting if she could come up to standards which she guessed would be high. She felt his arm come about her, knew the cool touch of his other hand as he took hers. A quiver that was pleasant ran along her spine, while anger filtered into her mind. She wanted to hate him!—

wished she could be told she was never to see him again, ever!

'You're very quiet.' His voice was strong, as usual, but low, against her ear. She had the impression that his chin was touching her hair—deliberately. Perhaps he was a flirt, and he fancied his chance with her in spite of what he had been told by Phil.

'I was thinking,' she replied briefly and non-committally.

'About what? Going home?'

'Perhaps,' she answered with a hint of defiance.

'Phil's relying on you.'

'He could easily get someone else.'

'Let's drop the subject,' he said curtly and they danced in silence until the music stopped. Clare, having managed to follow his steps perfectly, actually enjoyed the dance. He too enjoyed it, if he were to be believed when he said, 'Thank you, Clare. It was a pleasure to dance with you.'

She averted her face, telling herself that the embarrassment she felt was due rather to the unexpected compliment than the strangely soft inflection in his voice as he spoke her name. . . .

Phil suggested they take their coffee in the lounge but no sooner had they sat down than he was called away by one of his staff, and once again Clare found herself alone with Luke. He spoke first, breaking a silence which for Clare was fast becoming awkward.

'You're not really serious in your intention of going home, are you?'

'I haven't definitely made up my mind,' she replied. 'I did say I was only thinking about it.'

'It's morbid to dwell on the past.' Luke spoke almost harshly, as if he were delivering a stern rebuke. 'I said each new day is what you intend to make it. *You* wake every morning with the firm intention of being unhappy.'

'You know so much, don't you?' she retorted sarcastically.

'I know you're a fool!'

She glanced up; their eyes met fleetingly, hers wide, indignant and questioning, his narrowed and inscrutably dark.

'You baffle me,' she complained and looked away.

'Then that makes two of us. I've never met a woman like you.' He paused as if giving her the chance to speak. 'Do you really intend to remain sunk in misery for the rest of your life?'

She frowned in puzzlement. 'I've said you baffle me. I can't understand your concern.'

A strange silence ensued before Luke spoke, and when he did speak there was the most odd inflection in his voice.

'It could be that I don't understand it myself. Let's change the subject, shall we?' He glanced at her empty coffee cup. 'Better still, let us take a stroll. It's becoming far too hot in here.'

Clare hesitated; the last thing she wanted was to walk outside with him, in the lovely tropical gardens, with the bright stars above and the moon turning the wavelets to silver along the pink-sanded beach. But on the other hand, she had to remember that Luke was her brother's friend and, therefore, she must make some attempt to appear friendly.

'Why the hesitation?' challenged Luke with a touch of irony in his voice. 'Would you prefer to be alone, so that you can brood?'

Her mouth went tight. The insufferable man would rile her to the point of no return if he went on like this. It was with considerable difficulty that she managed to keep the anger from her tone as she said, 'Of course not. I shall enjoy a stroll in the fresh air.'

Faintly he smiled, as if fully aware that she was lying.

The cooling breeze of the trade winds fanned her face as, after walking along the pergola-shaded terrace in front of the lounge, they came into the gardens proper. Sounds drifted to her over the soft balmy air—the murmur of the waves breaking against the coral reef, the tender Bahamian music from the restaurant, the whisper of night creatures in the stately royal palms and the 'pity-pit-pit' call of a nighthawk as it swirled down from some unseen place high in the air. The beach was deserted, serene and unspoiled as it was hundreds of years ago, before man ever set foot on its virgin sand.

'It's a beautiful evening.' Clare spoke to break the silence which seemed to be becoming too companionable for her liking. She did not want to feel at ease with Luke; on the contrary, she desired only that they should both keep their distance from one another, being polite and nothing more. But somehow the situation was becoming out of control, with Luke acting as if he had the right to criticise and admonish, and to advise her to remain on the island. She thought about his comments and decided that she ought to remain, if only to give her parents a little peace of mind, something they certainly had not had for the past five years, knowing that, every Saturday, no matter what the weather, she would meet her dead fiancé's mother in the grim environment of the cemetery. Was it morbid to want to go there? Her father had said so, and now Luke had said it was morbid to dwell on the past. Neither of them understood, she told herself. Being men, they had no deep emotional feelings about such things as memories that were more precious than anything else in the world.

'Are you enjoying the stroll?' inquired Luke after agreeing with her that it was a beautiful evening. They were on the hotel's private beach, where tall coconut palms extended as far as the eye could see, and intriguing little lanes meandered in their midst before disappearing into the wooded grounds of the hotel.

'Yes,' answered Clare, 'I'm enjoying it very much.' She spoke the truth but wished she could have told herself she was lying.

'Shall we carry on? I have a feeling that Phil is not going to be able to leave his duties for a while.'

She nodded and said yes, she would like to go a little farther. As her gaze went out towards the horizon she was recalling her impression as she flew over from Nassau in the small aeroplane. The numerous islands and cays were strung out over a cerulean blue sea, jewels glistening in the sunlight. In the shallows beyond the Gulf Stream blue and green and silver mingled to produce unbelievable colours, while the Gulf Stream itself was a dark indigo blue edged with platinum where the crested waves lashed into foam.

She turned her head to glance up at the sphinx-like profile of the man at her side. So superior! Her first impression had been that he was totally unapproachable. With other women he seemed to be oblivious even of their presence; this she had noticed on several occasions when he had come to the hotel in the evening, perhaps to dine but sometimes merely to have a drink and a chat to Phil in the Yellow Bird Bar, a part of the hotel that had undergone a tasteful conversion from what had once been a slave kitchen, the place where all food was served to the numerous slaves working on the estate of the owner of the plantation house which was now the main building of the Rusty Pelican Hotel.

Luke glanced down at her and a smile suddenly lifted one corner of his mouth, robbing it of some of its severity.

'A penny,' he said, still looking at her. 'Or perhaps your thoughts are too critical for revealing.'

She drew a long breath.

'Are you always like this with women?' she could not help saying, 'or is it only with me?'

'Only with you,' came his prompt reply, disconcerting her.

'There must be a reason,' she murmured curiously after a pause.

'You intrigue me. A beautiful girl of twenty-five eating her heart out over someone who's been dead for five years.'

'That,' said Clare shortly, 'is my own affair!'

'You consider it indelicate of me to mention it?'

'I consider it interfering of you to mention it!' She stopped, wanting to turn back, but to her amazement Luke put his hand beneath her elbow and she was urged forward, along the soft pink coral sand. She felt that strange stirring within her again, because of the touch of his hand and the nearness of his body to hers. She trembled, her thoughts so confused as to be almost chaotic. She actually *liked* the nearness of his body, the rhythm he adopted in order to match his steps to hers, but on the other hand she was filled with resentment that he should make her forget the pledge she had made herself, and also the promise she had given Frank's mother. Yes, on more than one occasion she had assured Mrs Weedall that she would never let another man come into her life.

The air was still, suddenly, and all was silent around them. The high, rolling moon drifted through delicate threads of lacy cirrus cloud, shedding its argent glow over the sands and the

sea and the fringing reef. There was magic all
around . . . an intangible, spellbinding witchery
that enveloped Clare in spite of her determination to hold herself aloof from anything remotely
akin to the romantic. But she fought a losing
battle, the island alone casting a spell on her
with its Utopian enchantment, and if that
weren't enough she had as her companion this
tall handsome man whose personality was
breaking down her defences.

He spoke, softly, his head bent so that his
mouth was close to her ear, 'How easily your
anger's aroused, my child. Why don't you relax,
come out from that barrier you've built around
yourself and learn to laugh again?' He had
stopped, and they stood together, motionless and
silent for a few moments after he had spoken.
Clare lifted her head, her big hazel eyes wide
and bewildered and rather brighter than they
should be.

'I don't want to forget. . . .' Her voice faltered
to a slow stop, because of the sudden tightness
affecting her throat. 'You don't understand,
Luke. No one does. Frank adored me and I him.
You can't just forget—it isn't right to forget.'

She heard him draw a breath and guessed that
he was impatient with her.

'Five years, Clare,' he said. 'How much longer
are you going to pine for what you can't possibly
have?'

'You're wrong. I said you don't understand.
I'm not pining for something I can't have; that

would be absurd. I'm merely keeping a memory alive—'

'It'll fade, no matter how hard you try,' he broke in roughly. 'You might prolong the agony but in the end it will fade. You'll be a middle-aged spinster then and you'll have wasted your youth.'

'I don't know why you should be so concerned about me,' she quivered, staring into his eyes but finding neither compassion nor understanding. 'It's strange that you should be, because you don't strike me as a man who bothers his head much about my sex.'

'Well,' he returned with a light little laugh, 'that's forthright enough! So I strike you as a confirmed bachelor, do I?' There was an odd inflection in his voice which puzzled her. Had he had a serious affair, she wondered. After all, she knew nothing of his past; there could be some very good reason why, at thirty-five, he was still a bachelor.

She said, compelled by something she could not control, 'Have you ever been in love—?' She stopped abruptly, wishing she could take the words back.

'Sort of,' was his surprising answer. Clare had felt sure that even if he had been in love he would have flatly denied it. 'It was a long time ago.'

'It was . . . serious?'

He smiled reminiscently. 'Yes, it was—rather.'

Clare felt a little access of pity for him, which

was absurd, she chided herself, since Luke
Mortimer was the last man who needed pity. He
had everything—wealth, looks, physique, a
wonderful house here and another in fabulous
Miami Beach. And with all this he could have
any woman he wanted.

'Is she—alive?'

'I'm not pining over someone who is dead,
Clare.'

She coloured up. 'It was a silly question.
You've already stressed the futility of cherishing
memories.'

'You admit it's futile?'

'For me it isn't, but for you—'

'There's no difference,' he broke in impatiently.

Clare twisted round. 'I'm going back,' she
said, a flatness in her voice. Subconsciously she
had wanted to stay with him for a while longer
but, somehow, his impatience brought back her
resentment and she began to retrace her steps.
Luke set the pace, which was faster than she
desired. He had had enough of her company, she
thought, and an unwanted feeling of dejection
swept over her. She hurried along beside him,
skipping now and then to keep up the pace set by
those incredibly long legs of his. Her thoughts
wandered to the girl he had loved. Where was
she now? Was she married to someone else? Did
Luke still care—just a little?

Clare drew a deep, shuddering breath, and
wondered why her dejection should be even
more weighty than before.

Chapter Two

Another fortnight went by and to her own surprise Clare was becoming so contented that the
idea of going home scarcely ever entered her
mind. She loved the sun and the sea and the
lush, tropical vegetation of the island. Above all
she was enchanted with the unspoiled, un-
changing ways of the people, the natives who
lived in brightly-painted clapboard houses,
some of which nestled within groves of casuarinas, while others occupied sites in the narrow,
neat little tree-lined streets.

'These people have retained the secret of how
life should be lived,' Luke had told Clare after
she had remarked on the happy, contented faces
she invariably encountered whenever she went
out of the hotel grounds to explore the island. On
the main street there was one single traffic light,
and this was the only one on the island. Drivers
moved sedately towards it, hailing one another
as they passed. All was free and easy, unhurried
and leisurely. Clare had passed a remark to
Luke about his building programme and had

been assured that the people buying his properties would be carefully chosen; moreover, he was laying down certain conditions that would have to be adhered to. Each villa was to be inconspicuously sited among trees already established, and once built the houses could neither be altered nor added to in any way whatsoever.

'Will prospective purchasers agree to these restrictions?' Clare had asked doubtfully.

Luke had shrugged his shoulders and answered to the effect that if people disliked the restrictions imposed they would obviously decide not to buy.

'I particularly want to keep this island unspoiled,' he had gone on to say. 'The villas I shall build will not be a blot on the landscape, I can assure you of that.' He had smiled in a way that set her pulses stirring . . . and her resentment rising. It was all so absurdly illogical, she admitted, but her tenacious determination to cling to her memories, to be true to her lost love, seemed to be warping her vision and there was nothing she could do about it because, if she even contemplated seeing someone else she was immediately filled with guilt and a feeling of disloyalty both to Frank and to his mother.

Mrs Weedall had written to her, reiterating what she had said when she first learned of Clare's decision to join her brother on Flamingo Cay, 'I don't know how you could go away from everything you have known with Frank. And what about his grave? There'll be no one when

I've gone—' and at this point she had prophesied an early death for herself, because she had nothing left to live for now that her husband had died. Her other son, she said, had no feelings at all. 'He keeps telling me I'm morbid. Did you ever hear anything so unkind, dear Clare?'

Clare had read the letter and then wept for the loneliness of the woman who would have been her mother-in-law. On impulse she had invited her over for a holiday but as yet had received no reply to her letter.

On another occasion, when she had been in conversation with Luke, Clare had received an invitation from him to attend a sort of garden party which he was giving for prospective purchasers of his villas. They would be shown over his own house, advised about any internal changes they might require, and any other matters regarding the properties which might be of interest to them. Phil was also invited but at the last minute he decided he could not spare the time.

'You go, though,' he urged when Clare seemed hesitant about going on her own. 'It'll be a nice break for you. Mary can manage on the desk. It isn't as if we've anyone checking in until tomorrow morning.'

Still reluctant, Clare took a little more time over her lunch than usual, her mind occupied with the changes that were coming over her since she had joined her brother at the hotel. There was no doubt that the heaviness of the past years was lightening, that changes were taking place within her despite her struggles to prevent change. More and more she was thinking of Luke's words and admitting that he was right when he stated that the memory would fade. Yes, in time it would fade, if she remained here. But if she went home and took up where she had left off . . . A sudden frown touched her forehead at the thought. She had no desire to go back—at least not yet.

The colour-drenched gardens of Silver Springs presented an incredible panorama of tropical beauty, and as she gazed around Clare had to own that Luke Mortimer was nothing less than a genius where planning was concerned, be it a house he was planning or gardens such as these surrounding his villa, which itself was a breathtaking example of elegance and good taste.

She had arrived on foot, Silver Springs being no more than ten minutes' walk from the Rusty Pelican. Luke, casual but immaculate in white slacks and short-sleeved shirt, came striding across the satin-smooth lawn to meet her, his dark eyes taking in her own delightful appearance. She wore a sleeveless cotton dress, leaf-green and short, revealing her honey-tanned arms and legs. Her sandals were of fine white leather, matching her handbag and the wide belt she wore. Luke's eyes came at length to rest on her face; she parted her lips, unaware that the smile was delightfully reflected in her eyes, giving them a radiance Luke had never seen there before. His scrutiny was unfathomable and long, and she blushed delicately beneath it, even more so when his eyes began to move with slow deliberation to settle for a moment on the tiny waist before rising to the tender curves of her breasts and then higher to the gentle swell of her throat. He seemed to catch his breath and at the same time a nerve pulsated at the side of his neck. Fascinated by it, Clare wondered just what kind of emotion touched him for it to be reflected in this way.

'Clare,' he murmured softly at last, 'you look very charming. You'll be the most beautiful woman here today.'

Her colour deepened at his flattery and a tremor that was pleasant touched the region of her heart.

'Thank you, Luke,' she responded shyly. 'I'm glad you like my—my dress. . . .'

He laughed and her heart jerked involuntarily. Without doubt this man affected her senses on every occasion that they met, this in spite of her initial resolve to remain immune. His superlative physical attractions, the way his very tone of voice could give pleasure or pain, the expression she caught now and then that affected her pulse . . . all these were definite phases of her recent admission that Frank no longer held her entire waking thoughts, although he was, of course, ever in the background, an image that she never wanted completely to erase.

'Yes,' Luke was saying, breaking into her

reverie, 'I like your dress very much . . . but it wasn't your dress I was referring to, and you know it.'

She looked at him, a tiny frown between her eyes.

'I wasn't being facetious,' she retorted defensively.

'But you were,' he contradicted. And then, without warning, he reached to take her hand, just as he had done on two previous occasions. But whereas on those occasions she had snatched her hand away before he could touch it, this time she even made a shy movement to let him enclose it within the warmth of his lean brown fingers. The contact sent feathery ripples along her spine; her smile fluttered, then deepened and seemed to match the liquid glow of pleasure in her eyes.

'I—you. . . .' Her voice trailed off, partly because she had no idea what she wanted to say, and partly because that nerve was pulsating in Luke's throat again, and she could not take her eyes off it—not until, with a gentle finger beneath her chin, he lifted her face and she found herself staring into his eyes. The next instant he had bent his head and she felt the touch of a man's lips for the first time in five years. Sheer undiluted pleasure rippled through her before, out from the recesses of her mind, there emerged the image of her dead fiancé. . . .

Her mouth twisted convulsively as the past flared to reality and she lived again through poignant memory the happiness she and Frank had shared. And then Mrs Weedall's anguished face superimposed itself over everything else and Clare heard her own sincere promise that she would never let another man enter her life.

An involuntary shudder brought movement to Clare's body even before she fiercely snatched her hand away.

Luke's own hand fell to his side as, perceiving Clare's distress, his eyes glinted wrathfully. There was no hint of pity in his voice when presently he spoke.

'What's wrong now?' he demanded. 'You've changed dramatically within seconds.'

He knew of course what was wrong, but was determined to force an answer from her.

Her eyes lifted to his, pain mirrored in their depths.

'I know you've no—no patience w-with me,' she began, 'but—'

'Not a scrap of patience!' he broke in derisively. 'You're your own worst enemy, and no one can help you!'

She stared with bewildered incomprehension, noticing the tightness of his mouth, the flexed line of his jaw, the narrowed, uncompromising expression in those steely grey eyes.

'You shouldn't have held my hand!' she flashed, forgetting her own reciprocation. 'There was no need!'

'Memories!' he scoffed, containing his temper with the utmost effort. 'One day, Clare, I shall lose my control and knock some sense into you!'

'You—!' Staggered by his imperious manner

Clare could only stare at him for a long disbelieving moment. 'What did you say?' she challenged at last.

'You heard! Next time you'll *feel!*'

An astounded silence followed this incredible threat, an upsurge of anger bringing colour to her cheeks. Anyone would think he had some sort of authority over her, the way he spoke!

'Don't you dare speak to me like that!' she fumed. 'Who do you think you are—adopting that high-handed attitude with me?'

Luke glowered at her, then suddenly his manner changed, and when he spoke he had assumed an air of indifference that was as unexpected as it was incomprehensible.

'You are quite right to be indignant. I've no reason at all for my—er—high-handed attitude as you term it.' His eyes roved her with a hint of contempt before he added briskly. 'Come along. I don't know what we're standing here for!'

He began to walk away and Clare hurried to keep up with him. She was miserable because of his changed manner and because of her own reaction to the simple affectionate gesture of his taking her hand. He had obviously wanted to take it, expecting to derive some kind of pleasure, and she too had been in a reciprocal frame of mind until that intrusion of the past had filled her whole being with a sense of disloyalty and guilt. Would it continue for ever? Until coming here to Flamingo Cay she had not wanted it to end; her memories were carrying her through and, as far as her mind could estimate, they would go on doing so for the rest of her life. After all, she had told herself, there were other women who, true to a first love, had remained single when that first love died. Clare knew of one middle-aged spinster who, having lost her boy-friend in the war, had remained wholly true to his memory.

They reached the courtyard, created by Luke's ingenuity from the natural coral rock, and Clare stopped to stare appreciatively at the flowers— exotic orchids set delightfully in the low branches of the trees, the flaring hibiscus blossoms, the blood red canna lilies. The two crystal fountains sparkled in the sunshine, music in their cascading descent from the low cliffs of gleaming coral limestone.

'It's lovely,' breathed Clare, lifting her eyes to Luke's face. 'You have a marvellous flair for creating beauty. Men are not usually appreciative of such things.'

'You think not?' with a lift of his faintly-arched brows. 'I can assure you, Clare, that most men do certainly appreciate beauty.'

There was no mistaking his meaning and Clare glanced away, profoundly sensitive to the fact that his anger had dissolved, and yet repelled—in some way which she owned was quite illogical—from encouraging anything closer than this superficial friendliness he was now adopting. She must not allow him to take her hand again, and most certainly she would never allow him to kiss her.

She glanced up at him, wondering if he expected her to make some comment. However, he spoke again before she could, a hint of mockery in his deep male voice.

'I expect, my dear, that you would like me to change the subject.' She said nothing and after a small pause he went on, 'You're not immune to male flattery, Clare, although you'd very much like to convince me that you are.' Again there was no response and he made no further attempt to draw her out, but instead he invited her into the house for a drink. 'You're early,' he added as she fell into step beside him as he proceeded in the direction of an open French window leading into the living-room of the villa, 'and so I can spare you a little of my time. The few people who are already here are with my agent; he's giving them a rough outline of our intentions regarding the development of the land we've bought.'

'They're round at the other side of the house?' She had heard voices so concluded the agent and his audience were there.

Luke nodded his head. 'Yes. He'll keep them occupied until others arrive.'

Once inside the house Luke took Clare into the living-room and after seeing her seated in a big armchair he asked her what she would like to drink.

'A large lemonade, please,' she answered, 'with ice.'

'It shall be done.' He walked away and she glanced around.

It was a delightful room furnished with taste and at a great expense, but in its male and austere atmosphere something vital to complete comfort was lost. Clare's roving eye assessed what was missing and without realizing it she was mentally effecting improvements that would produce the character and cosiness which it lacked at present. She would have flowers here, and cushions there, and a few more rugs to break up the exquisite marble tiling of the floor. An old master would look just right over there, with a light playing on it from above. An antique Chelsea group similar to one owned by a friend would indeed set off the piecrust table standing to one side of the window—

'What are you thinking about?' Luke's deep voice broke into a reverie that was exceedingly pleasant and she glanced up to see him standing there by the cocktail cabinet, a glass of iced lemonade in his hand. She coloured delicately, wondering what he would say if she answered his question truthfully. She had no intention of doing so and she prevaricated by smilingly telling him how much she liked the room. He glanced about him and to her surprise she saw a frown appear between his eyes. Perhaps, she thought, he too realised that it lacked a woman's touch.

He sat down on a chair opposite to her and they chatted while having their drinks. He was amicable enough but there was a certain coolness about him which she knew resulted from her own attitude.

It came as a complete surprise, therefore,

when he invited her to dine at his home that evening.

'I'm on my own,' he added before she could speak, 'I shall enjoy the company.'

'On your own?' she repeated without knowing why.

'Yes, on my own,' he said, a sort of mocking challenge in his glance. 'Afraid of something?'

'Why should I be afraid?' she countered, but she looked away, avoiding his eyes, and focused her attention on a dainty little humming-bird flashing its iridescent plumage among the crimson flowers of a hibiscus bush.

'Perhaps,' rejoined Luke tersely, '*you* can tell *me* why you should be afraid?'

Clare sent him a frowning glance and said indignantly, 'The question ought never to have been asked, so why throw it back at me?'

There was a long, impatient moment of silence before Luke, regarding her squarely, asked if he considered that the whole of her life and future were owed to a man who was dead. Clare flinched and shook her head. It was not a negative gesture but one of bewilderment and uncertainty. For although she had wanted Luke to hold her hand just now, and had enjoyed his kiss, she had immediately been stabbed by a sense of guilt as memories intruded. Then there was the solemn promise she had made to Frank's mother, a promise which had undoubtedly brought some small measure of comfort to an old lady whose life was empty now that she had lost her husband as well as her son.

Miserably Clare looked up, tears pricking the backs of her eyes.

'I don't know, Luke,' she faltered. 'I'm so confused.'

Luke drew an impatient breath which somehow nettled her, causing her to turn on him and say fiercely, 'Why don't you mind your own business! What are you trying to do to me?'

'Make you see sense!' he returned with sudden harshness. 'Why don't you snap out of it and learn to live again?'

Clare's eyes blazed, but before she had time to say what was in her mind, Luke, with a couple of long determined strides, had covered the distance between them; one hand shot out to grip her wrist while with the other he took the glass from her and put it on the table, spilling the liquid as he did so. Clare, frozen into immobility by surprise at his unexpected action, was roughly jerked against his hard body without as much as a cry of protest, let alone any physical resistance.

'Yes,' he gritted determinedly, 'it's time you learned to live again—and I'm just the man to give you a few lessons!' His dark face was close; she felt his cool clean breath fanning her cheek, was conscious of tempting after-shave lotion, pine-scented and fresh. The sudden contact of his sensuous mouth sent a spasm of pleasure through her body yet at the same time galvanised her into action and her struggles began as she twisted about, attempting to free herself from a hold that was steel-hawser strong. She managed to press her hands against the iron-hardness of his chest but when she felt the strong wiry hairs through the thin cotton of his shirt she gave a shudder and brought her hands away again, far more swiftly than she had put them there.

'Let me go!' she cried when he took his lips from hers. 'You're a cad to do this to me—!'

'Don't be trite,' he admonished, a hint of mocking amusement in his tone. He looked into her eyes for a long unfathomable moment and then, 'Defiance . . . resistance . . . that's what I see in these lovely eyes—' He touched the lids as they came down protectively against his caressing fingers. 'But I shall see desire—yes, the dreamy dark pools that tell me you're not the little iceberg you'd have everyone believe. Five years! My God, child, it's a lifetime! And with your beauty—'

'I'm not beautiful!' she broke in fiercely. 'I'm not!'

'You with your *exquisite* beauty,' he continued, ignoring the interruption, 'growing old all the time! I shan't let you lose what life and love can give!'

'Love?' She shook her head. 'I shall never fall in love! Nor do I want anyone to fall in love with me! You know why—so stop torturing me! Let me go—'

'Your body's made for pleasure—a man's pleasure as well as your own—'

'Stop it! Listen to what I have to say!' Tears rolled unchecked down her cheeks but he was immune to them. 'You're a beast! I shall tell my brother what you've done to me!'

'I don't think so,' he disputed imperturbably. 'This, Clare, is between you and me.' His mouth, full-lipped and demanding, sensuous and moist, pressed hard against the quivering, convulsive movement of hers, his tongue exploring, his hands caressing, his hard virile body arched, melding its dominant strength to her slender frame.

Clare began to struggle again, tears of mortification rolling down her face as he gave a low triumphant laugh at her puny, futile efforts.

'I enjoy showing you my strength.' His voice was a throaty bass murmur against her ear. 'And you . . . Doesn't a woman enjoy the sensation of weakness, of being mastered?'

'No!'

'Liar! I'm no callow youth without experience,' he assured her with a touch of arrogant mastery. 'My experience of women taught me long ago that there's still a trait within them that's a legacy from the primitive, from caveman times—'

'Don't talk such rubbish!' she flared. 'And I'm not interested in your experience with women in any case!'

He looked deeply into her eyes. 'You're even more desirable when you're angry,' he mused. 'How is it that no man has drawn the sword against your defences before now?' Without giving her time to answer, his lips possessed hers again, his body crushing hers with the

calculated intention of forcing her to experience
the feel of his male hardness. His muscles were
flexed against the softness of her thighs, while
the ravaging dominance of his mouth explored
her throat, discovering a hypersensitive place
with his tongue and in spite of her instinct to
struggle Clare found herself carried irresistibly
on the tide of his ardour as spasm after spasm
rocked her whole frame, reducing her limbs to
pulp as the fire of his passion razed her defences
to ashes. His hand moved in sensual exploration
of her imprisoned body and when her small firm
breast was captured and caressed a low moan of
ecstasy escaped her and she clung to him as
mind and body drifted into a sensuous torpor
with every vestige of strength deserting her.

At last he held her from him, triumph mingling with mockery to create an expression that
she ought to have resented but could not. Instead she lowered her head to find a resting
place for it on his chest. She was still clinging to
him, sensuously gripped in the afterglow of his
violent love-making.

She felt his hand caressing her hair and,
strangely comforted, she pressed just a little bit
closer to him.

'Let me look into your eyes,' Luke ordered
presently, and at the same time he was gently
cupping her chin to raise her head. A mocking
smile quirked one corner of his mouth as he
said, softly and yet with an inflection of triumph
in his voice, 'Dark and dreamy . . . result of

those most pleasant sensations that coursed
through your veins just now—'

'Don't!' she implored, her sweet full mouth
twisting convulsively. 'Please don't gloat, Luke;
I can't bear it.'

The grey eyes narrowed and for one despairing moment she thought he was going to
drop the tender way he was adopting with her.
She felt she would have wept unrestrainedly if
he had, but it seemed as if he perceived her fears
and it was with infinite gentleness that he
brought her head to his breast again, stroking
her hair, fingering the tender places close to her
ear and finally embracing her quietly, and without passion.

'I'm not gloating,' he assured her softly. 'But I
am trying to point out the fact that you are by no
means as cold and unemotional as you yourself
believe. On the contrary, were you to drop every
single inhibition, you'd be the most desirable
lover any man could wish for.'

Clare wanted to protest, to stop him in the
middle of what he was saying, but she was still
in a state of torpor, wanting only to rest her body
and relax her mind. It must be wonderful, she
thought dreamily, to make love and then sleep in
your lover's arms, your naked body close to his.
The thought was thrust away determinedly.
Marriage was not for her—no, not even though
she had been taught so much in the last few
minutes. She leant away, realising that it was
with a tremendous effort that she was keeping

Frank and his mother out of her mind. Both had intruded in the last half minute or so but their images were vague, nebulous, almost.

'What are you thinking about?' Luke wanted to know, his eyes narrowing again. 'Tell me.'

She shook her head.

'I'm trying not to think about anything,' she admitted.

The grey eyes became perceptive, and faintly wrathful.

'Then keep on trying,' he advised tautly. 'Forget the past!'

Clare said nothing, because she had no wish to make him angry with her. But she had no intention of heeding him; she had pledged her word to Frank's mother and she had no intention of breaking that pledge. In any case, her love for her dead fiancé had not waned even though the years had, to a great extent, assuaged the pain. She owed it to him to remain faithful to his memory because, as his mother always reminded her, had the positions been reversed Frank would never even have looked at another woman.

'Clare,' said Luke, breaking into her train of thought, 'are you going to accept that invitation to dine with me?'

Without hesitation she shook her head, drawing right away from him. 'No, Luke, I'd rather not.'

'You can't still be afraid,' he snapped irritably, 'not after what has just happened.'

'It's not fear,' she told him simply.

'Memories!' The fury in his voice was as violent as it was unexpected and she took another protective step away from him. 'God, Clare, if I don't end up by beating you it will be a miracle!'

Chapter Three

Quite naturally his words hammered in Clare's brain for a long time after she had left the garden party. Luke, his impatience stronger than his gallantry, had left her severely alone, chatting to the others who had attended the gathering. It seemed to matter not at all to him that she was wandering about on her own, and even when he did happen to run across her somewhere in the grounds he merely nodded his head abruptly and went over to speak to someone else. It was entirely her own fault, she knew, and after an hour spent in appreciation of the grounds and the house—she had joined a group taken into the house by the agent—she sought Luke out to tell him she was leaving.

'As you wish,' was his only comment before saying an abrupt goodbye.

She walked back to the hotel slowly, along the beach, the sand talcum-soft and warm from the sun. She went over in detail all that had happened to her during the relatively short time she had been Luke's guest. That he had awakened latent emotions she could not very well deny, and she was realistic enough to admit that, should he again tempt her, her defences would be no stronger than they were today. The obvious solution was to make sure she avoided such a vulnerable and dangerous situation in the future.

Her mind-wanderings always came back to his threat about a beating. Why should he adopt such a masterful, proprietorial attitude towards her? Undoubtedly he had taken it upon himself to make a concerted effort to break down her persistence in cherishing a memory. Resentment flooded over her. He had no right to meddle in her affairs, and by the time she arrived back at the Rusty Pelican she was so angry that she sought out her brother and demanded to know why he had confided her affairs to a stranger.

'Luke isn't a stranger,' corrected Phil. He was on the patio, attired in shorts and a crisp white cotton shirt. It was a quiet period for the hotel because the off-season was just beginning and so it was now possible for Phil to relax, something he rarely did. Clare, looking at him sitting on the lounger, wondered how she could ever be vexed with him. He was so kind and gentle, with ways very different from those of his friend.

Clare could never imagine his being as rough with a girl as Luke had been with her a few hours earlier. Frank had been like Phil—gentle and, at times, a little unsure of himself, even though he had secured the post of deputy-head of his school. 'He's a good friend, Clare, even though we haven't known one another very long.' Phil paused a moment, his attention arrested by splashes of colour from bikini-clad figures on the sun-terrace where the graceful fronds of a coconut palm danced against a background of sapphire blue sky. 'You and he puzzle me, Clare. One moment you appear to be getting along all right and the next there's a sort of hostile atmosphere between you which could almost be cut with a knife.' He looked at her, his keen gaze all-examining. 'Something's happened. You're back early from the party. I hope you haven't quarrelled with him,' he added anxiously.

'Not exactly.' Her voice was stiff, and he shook his head, frowning at her.

'What happened, Clare?'

She had taken possession of a lounger opposite him but, filled with sudden restlessness, she rose again to pace the patio, wondering what Phil would have to say if she were to give him an account of what had occurred.

'Luke seems to be extraordinarily interested in me,' she said at length. 'He appears to think he can make me forget the past.' She spoke quietly and without emotion, marvelling at the swiftness with which she had regained her calm. She knew she had been pale after leaving Luke's house, for a glance in the mirror as she came into the lobby of the Rusty Pelican revealed an unusual pallor, but now there was a fresh bloom on her cheeks, and her brother's eyes, she noticed, were appreciative.

'It's my fault, I'm afraid, Clare.' The admission left Phil's lips slowly, reluctantly. Clare glanced interrogatingly at him and moved towards the lounger again.

'Your fault? How can that be? I know you've told him about Frank, and that I mean to keep his memory green, but—'

'I also asked him if he would try to make you see the folly of it all,' Phil confessed. 'Mother wrote and begged me to do everything in my power to restore you to normal—'

'Normal?' she echoed indignantly.

'Well,' he pointed out, 'it's scarcely normal for anyone to pine for over five years, is it?'

'I'm not pining!'

He shrugged, and leant forward to take up a packet of cigarettes from a small pinewood table by his feet.

'Call it what you like,' he said, 'but it's certainly been a blight on Mother's life—and Dad's, because if she suffers he does too. They're so close, always have been.'

A sigh escaped Clare as she sat down, refusing Phil's offer of a cigarette. Her eyes strayed momentarily to the classic beauty of islands rising from the sea—summits of a huge massif, the underwater mountains of the Bahamas.

'So that is the reason for Luke's attitude towards me,' she mused, wondering why she should be feeling so flat all at once. 'His only interest in me stems merely from the request you made. . . .' Her eyes strayed now to a less distant scene—a little building that was connected with the hotel but standing in its own delightful grounds where hibiscus, poinsettia, crotons and numerous other exotic plants mingled to create a tableau of colour against a backcloth of traveller's palms. The Clipper Inn, whose quaint dormer windows were framed by pink bougainvillaea which climbed almost to the gabled roof, then dropped again to shower the trellised porch and low verandahs.

'He promised to do whatever he could.' Her brother's voice brought her eyes back to his handsome, sun-bronzed face.

'At first, though,' Clare reflected thoughtfully, 'he didn't take much notice of me at all.'

'I didn't make the request right away. Mother's letter came after you'd been here about three weeks, and I didn't quite know how I was to do anything at all, then suddenly I hit on the idea that Luke might just be able to help. . . .' He trailed off with a little self-deprecating sigh. 'It wasn't a good idea, evidently. You resent the way he goes about it?'

'He's so high-handed and—and—bossy.'

'It's his way. Luke's one of those men who,

when dealing with women, adopts an attitude of—well—superiority, for the want of a better word.'

'Why should he feel superior?' she flashed. 'Who does he think he is, I'd like to know!'

'It's just his way,' repeated Phil gently. 'Some men feel they're the dominant sex, and they act accordingly.'

Clare's hazel eyes glinted. 'He's old-fashioned. The days of masculine assertion are gone—'

'Don't you believe it. Man orders and woman obeys. Nature ordained it that way.' The smoothly-spoken interruption came from the end of the patio, where Luke, tall, assured and with a mocking light in his eyes as they settled on Clare's flushed face, had obviously been standing for a moment or two before breaking into what Clare was saying. Languidly he came forward and Phil invited him to sit down, glancing at Clare a little uncertainly as if in doubt as to whether or not he was doing the right thing in asking his friend to join them. Her expression was a mere mask, so Phil was unable to read anything from it, but Luke appeared to be vastly amused by her stolid mien. He had obviously got over his ill-humour, she thought, refusing to meet his gaze as he sat down opposite her.

'Luke—I didn't expect you at this time.' Phil spoke into the silence, his anxious eyes sliding again in his sister's direction. 'Is the party over?'

'My agent's there. I came away a little early. Jeff's more than capable of carrying on.' Lean-

ing back in the chair he stretched his long legs
out in front of him. 'I've bought an island,' he
remarked casually and Clare did glance at him
then, repeating involuntarily, 'An island? In the
Bahamas?'

He nodded, his sidelong glance flicking her
face.

'Windward Cay; it's a mile long and three
quarters of a mile wide.'

'You've bought a whole island?' The very idea
fascinated Clare and she forgot everything except her interest in what she had just heard. 'It's
all yours?'

'All mine,' he replied, amused at her expression.

She stared, her thoughts sliding for the moment to what her brother had been telling her.
She now knew the reason for Luke's interest in
her, but where had he got the idea of going about
it in that particular way? She wondered again
what her brother would think if she were to tell
him the method Luke had adopted—that he had
made love to her.

'What do you intend doing with it?' Phil
dragged lightly on his cigarette and blew a
smoke ring. 'Is it inhabited?'

'Surely the Bahamian Government doesn't
sell islands,' put in Clare, now doubtful and
half-believing that Luke was pulling their legs.

'It was privately owned already,' he explained.
'Some of the small islands are. We have seven
hundred islands in the group, remember.'

'A good number are tiny, and uninhabited,' said Phil.

'Of course. You always get tiny, uninhabited islands in a large chain like the Bahamas.'

Clare sat listening to this interchange, her eyes pensive and wide as they scanned the immediate scene of tropical elegance in the hotel gardens. Smooth lawns and exotic borders, mango trees and avocados, and a splendid hedge of pink hibiscus bushes. A huge fountain played in the middle of a paved area where roses grew in the circles and squares cut out for them. All along one side of the extensive grounds dark palm fronds were silhouetted against a sapphire sky where a few wispy cirrus clouds floated like fragments of pearl-white chiffon in the vast vault of the heavens.

'So you're going to develop it?' Phil's voice drifted over to Clare and she turned to look at him. The cigarette was between his fingers; he was bronzed and healthy, his hair at the front bleached by the sun.

'Yes, I intend to develop it.'

'And spoil it in the process?' The words were out before Clare could stop them and she received a scathing glance as Luke said curtly, 'I've never spoiled anything in my life—not to my knowledge—and I've no intention of doing so now.'

Rebuked, she fell silent, her eyes focusing on a small group of guests from the hotel who were playing beach ball on the smooth, silken sand. Several white-sailed yachts rested languidly not far from the shore, and farther out a water skier was having the time of his life.

'A resort for Senior Citizens? I think it's a wonderful idea!' Phil's enthusiastic comment brought Clare's attention back to the men's conversation. 'It must be an entirely new concept in the field of travel?'

Luke nodded his head.

'I had the idea some time ago but wasn't quite sure how to put it into operation. Then I heard of this island coming up for sale and put in an offer for it. Until recently it was inhabited by two families, both with a common distant relative who died and left them a fortune. They're Bahamians who'd been living on what they grew, mainly, and when this money came to them they decided to live in Nassau, and the island consequently came on the market. It seemed an ideal location for my experiment.'

'Where does it lie in relation to Flamingo Cay?'

'About twenty miles to the southeast.'

'Funny; I've never even heard of it.'

Luke gave a low laugh.

'There are dozens of islands and cays around here which I myself have never heard of. I often look at the map and find something new.'

Clare spoke at last, to ask about the project he had in mind.

'You weren't listening,' he chided, then added after a small pause, 'I'll tell you all about it over dinner this evening.'

'I'm not coming; I told you I wasn't.'

'I'm coming here. Any objection?'

She coloured up but before she had time to think of a suitable retort Phil was speaking. 'What's wrong with you two? It's time you buried the hatchet—whatever it might be.'

'We like our arguments, Phil. They add spice to life.'

Clare turned away, but Luke asked again if she had any objection to his coming to the Rusty Pelican to dine.

'I don't believe there are any restrictions on who shall or who shall not book a table here,' she returned shortly. 'Do you want the Tavern or the Steak Cellar?'

'Which do *you* prefer?'

'I'm dining with Phil in the Tavern Restaurant—where we always dine.'

'The Tavern it shall be,' he said affably. 'I'll see you both later.' And with that he got up from the chair, bade them goodbye and left.

'Does he have to be at our table?' she said pettishly to her brother.

'We can hardly give him a table on his own! I'd very much like to know what's wrong with you two. Has he done something really serious?'

She could almost have laughed. And yet . . . was his behaviour 'really serious'? She had reciprocated after a few initial protests and struggles, so what had she to complain about?

'No,' she murmured avoiding her brother's searching eyes, 'he's not done anything really serious. It's just that we rub one another up the wrong way.'

'Well, please don't quarrel with him,' her

brother begged. 'I enjoy his friendship and would be upset if anything happened to put an end to it.'

'I'll make sure that nothing does happen,' she promised and, after a small pause, 'Do you mind if I don't have dinner with you this evening, Phil? I'd rather have it in my room.'

'I'd rather you didn't,' was his blunt reply. 'Luke would take your absence as a snub. And by the way,' he added as the thought came to him, 'what did you mean by saying you weren't coming?'

'He'd invited me to have dinner at Silver Springs.'

'And of course you refused,' Phil eyed her impatiently. 'I wish I knew what was going on!'

'You do know what's going on. You asked him to do something to make me forget the past, and he's adopted this domineering attitude towards me.'

Phil regarded her curiously. 'What has he said to you?'

She shrugged her shoulders. 'It doesn't matter. I can deal with him.' She was far from sure but she tried to convince herself. The obvious thing to do, she had already decided, was to avoid being alone with him. That would effectively prevent any repetition of what had happened earlier this afternoon.

Although dress was casual Luke arrived in collar and tie, the white collar and cuffs of his shirt accentuating the deep rich bronze of his skin. Clare saw him enter the lounge and order a drink; she was in an alcove behind the bar, and as always she felt the effect of his personality, the sheer magnetism of him, the superlative way he dressed and carried himself, with an air of confidence which surpassed by far that of any other man she had ever met. Tremors—pleasant and yet unwanted—affected her senses, and her heart was beating in unison with the increased rate of her pulse.

He glanced around and she stepped back, reappearing again at the other side of the bar, from which she approached his table.

'Ah, there you are. I was beginning to wonder if you'd decided to take dinner in your room. It's just the kind of thing you would do.'

'I admit I had thought of it,' she returned with a sort of acid sweetness, 'but my brother decided it might be regarded by you as a snub.'

'Just as you would have meant it to be.' His full-lipped mouth quirked mockery at her. 'Sit down and have a drink.' He had risen when she reached the table and now, as she sat down, he moved to the chair facing her, beckoning to a passing waiter at the same time. Clare told him her choice and he ordered. A waiter brought a menu and another the wine list. 'Where's Phil?' he inquired. 'I thought the place was slack just now.'

'He'll be here presently.' She looked at him, recalling his behaviour of this afternoon and

wondered why she was not feeling embarrassed.

'I've something to propose to you,' he said
when her drink had arrived. 'This island—
Windward Cay—' He paused a moment, considering. 'How would you like to help me with it?'

'Help?' Clare glanced swiftly at him, her eyes
puzzled. 'What do you mean?'

'I'm developing it as a haven for those older
people who, these days, want to get away from
other people's children and can't. Do you realise
that there isn't one travel company who caters
for them?'

'I hadn't given it a thought,' admitted Clare.
'But now that you've mentioned it, it brings
something to mind. I knew of three old-aged
pensioners—three couples, I mean—who always
used to go away together. They've been doing it
for many years. Well, for the last four years
they've been trying, without success, to discover
somewhere really peaceful—a hotel where they
can find the sort of quiet that older people want.'
She paused, noticing that Luke was nodding,
absorbing with keen interest every word she
spoke. 'They were telling me that although they
liked children and all have grandchildren, they
want to get away from children—and the noise
they invariably make—for their annual holidays. The result of the four years' search is that
they've all decided never to go away again
during the school holidays.'

'But these days people don't mind keeping

their children out of school. One finds children in the hotels at all times of the year.'

'That's right, and so it doesn't give older people a chance.'

'I actually know of couples who have decided not to go away at all. The trouble is that the cheap package deals offer reduced rates for children—or even accept them at no cost at all. This is fine and I agree with it wholeheartedly because people with children must be catered to, but so must the elderly, the Senior Citizens. They've often brought up families, and perhaps as often cared for grandchildren; it's not unreasonable that they should want peace and quiet away from children entirely, when they take a holiday.'

'Most pensioners have a limited amount to spend, and as a result they've no alternative than to take those cheap package tours that offer special fares for children.'

'That's right. Well, I'm considering a non-profit scheme, so that it will be possible for people to come from Europe, not just the United States.'

Clare looked at him with deep admiration. This man was very different from the one she had known up till now, the astute businessman who, already a millionaire, was still looking for the means to make more money. She noticed the faraway look in his eyes, the softness where hard contours had been, the relaxed line of his jaw. Her pulses quivered as a tremor of yearning rippled through her. The power he had over her was incredible! It was difficult to take her eyes off him, and even more difficult to hide her feelings from that shrewd, perceptive gaze.

'You really want me to help you?' she queried, breaking the silence.

'I do, Clare. I'm building three hotels altogether, but two initially, all on the southern side of the island. That's not by any means overcrowding. There'll be acres of gardens surrounding each hotel. I plan to have every facility for amusement within the complex itself but the guests will be able to go from one hotel to another for entertainment and even food.'

'You mean, they can dine at any of the three hotels?'

'That's right, but of course they'll have to book in advance.'

'It sounds too good to be true,' she breathed, leaning forward and looking up into his face. 'Will there be tennis and golf and such things?'

'Everything they could want for passing a pleasant time within the precincts of the hotel. Of course, they can come and go as they like, but there isn't much room on the island for long tramps,' he added on a note of amusement. 'You can walk from one end to the other in less than half an hour.'

'Shall you be able to have floor shows?'

'I do plan to have a floor show once a week at each hotel, and that's why I'm making it possible for people to interchange for dinner—and all

the other meals if they so wish. But with
dinner—well, there are bound to be many
Darbys and Joans who will want to dine cosily
and romantically by candlelight and so they can
get away from the floor show if they want.' He
stopped slowly and she saw that he was lost in
dreams. What a surprising man! An idealist
when she had branded him hard and calculat-
ing, believing him to be a man who would not
stop at spoiling an island if by so doing he could
put wealth into his pocket. How very wrong she
had been!

'You've not told me yet how I can help,' she
reminded him. 'We digressed, I think.'

Luke brought his attention back to her, his
dark eyes unfathomable as he watched her sip
her drink. Clare met his gaze, half-inclined to
tell him that she knew why he was wanting her
to assist, that it was in order to help her forget
the past. But she decided against it, since it was
of no importance anyway. She had no intention
of forgetting the past.

'I would like you to take over, completely, the
decor and furnishings of all three hotels,' he told
her, smiling in some amusement at her gasp of
disbelief.

'Really, Luke! You really want to give me all
that responsibility?'

'I know you can do it,' was all he said by way of
answering her. 'I've already got everything else
moving.'

She looked at him from over the rim of her

glass, and his eyes flickered with humour again at her eagerness. But she was thinking of her job and wondering how she would fit in all the extra work. She had a good deal of time off, though, and every week-end she was relieved by Mary.

'It sounds fabulous, Luke! Oh, I shall love having a free hand to decorate and furnish to my own taste!' She had forgotten what he had done to her earlier, forgotten everything as already her brain was working, making pictures of lovely rooms tastefully equipped by her alone. Oh, but it really was something to look forward to!

'I take it,' remarked her companion suavely, 'that you've accepted the commission?'

She laughed . . . and noticed that nerve in his neck pulsating.

'I couldn't possibly refuse! I know it's going to be hard work, doing two jobs, but as I have plenty of spare time I'm sure I can manage.'

'That's my girl—' He broke off abruptly as if he realised he ought not to have said it. She sent him a startled glance, wishing she could read his thoughts. My girl. . . . He was coolly beckoning a waiter and Clare decided that it was merely a figure of speech which meant nothing. Yet why had he stopped so abruptly? In fact, his whole manner was strange, she now realised. Some sixth sense seemed to be telling her that there could be an altogether different reason for his interest in her. . . .

Chapter Four

'So Windward Cay will be advertised as suitable for Senior Citizens *only*?' Clare and Phil and Luke had been discussing the new project all through dinner, and as Phil put the question he was already preparing to leave them, as he had work to do in his office, he said.

'That's the idea.'

'Well, you have my good wishes,' returned Phil. 'And in addition any help I can give.'

'I'll remember that,' smiled Luke. 'I might need it.'

'See you later perhaps?' Phil glanced at his sister, plainly relieved that she and Luke were no longer at loggerheads. He had initially been taken aback on being told of Luke's offer to Clare, but almost immediately a perceptive glance at his sister revealed that he was assuming what she herself had first assumed: Luke was doing this in order to help Clare forget the past. 'Will you be in the lounge?'

Luke glanced at Clare. 'Would you like a drink

afterwards?' He and Clare had just ordered more coffee and were waiting for it to arrive.

'Yes—all right.' She was happy and it showed. Luke's expression was one of satisfaction and, later, when they were seated in the candle-lit lounge, in a secluded corner by a window overlooking the sea, he remarked on her enthusiasm.

'You know, Clare,' he added after a pause, 'you do have a zest for life, in spite of the way you've been for so many years.'

'I wanted to die once,' she reflected, not meaning to say anything like that but it just came out.

'Forget it!' he said peremptorily. 'You're young and life is for living.'

She nodded her head, affected as always by his magnetic personality. He really was something out of the ordinary, and she had early in their acquaintanceship realised that she was not the only one affected by his superlative qualities, for he invariably attracted feminine attention, with the very natural result that she was conscious of an inner glow of pride when, as now, she happened to be with him. She had discovered that in spite of her pledge she was still all woman, able to enjoy the envy of her sex.

'Life is different now,' she admitted, shy all at once and a little unsure of herself. 'I'm glad I came here.'

'So am I, Clare,' he returned slowly. 'Phil told me about your going to that churchyard every week. Well, that's no longer possible. It was a morbid thing to do anyway.' His voice was stern, admonishing and, strangely, she was unable to resent it.

'I suppose so, but it's hard to make a man understand. . . .'

Where was she going—drifting away from her memories like this, admitting that to go to the grave every week-end was morbid? She frowned at her thoughts and, glancing at her companion, suddenly found a response in the quick knitting of his brow.

'Drink up,' he ordered curtly, 'and we'll take a stroll outside.'

She shook her head, on her guard instantly, remembering her resolve. 'I don't want—'

'I'll not rape you,' he broke in, laughing at her expression. 'At least, not unless you want me to.'

'Stop it!' she cried, aware that she had coloured from her neck upwards. 'Do you have to spoil everything by saying things like that?'

He studied her curiously. 'It spoils . . . what, Clare?' he wanted to know, an odd inflection in his voice.

'Well. . . .' She had no immediate answer to a question that took her by surprise. 'We were getting along,' she added, because she herself was evading an answer.

'So we were.' His dark eyes still focused her face as he went on, a hint of mockery in his finely-timbered voice, 'I must learn to guard my tongue, so that we can continue to get along.' He rose as he spoke; she had finished her drink and with an inperious gesture he brought her up with him, his strong brown fingers transmitting the magic touch of ecstasy as they curled firmly around hers. Was she playing with fire? It was far too romantic out there, in the tropical gardens of the hotel. Lonely and quiet and mysterious. You felt you had the whole wide world to yourself; she knew because she had walked there alone many times since coming to work for her brother.

'I . . . it's late,' she faltered, trying to hold back. 'I feel rather tired—'

'Not tired,' he broke in with a hint of sardonic amusement, 'only scared.' He tugged at her hand, compelling her to follow him in obedience to the command of the gesture. 'I don't think I've ever met a woman as scared as you,' he added over his shoulder. 'It's time you took a good look at yourself—and effected an improvement.'

'I'm not scared!' she denied. 'Why should I be?'

'Because you're sensitive to fear.' They were approaching an open French window and he fell silent until they were through it and some distance from it, then he stopped, looking down at her in the muted lights from the coloured lanterns in the trees. 'It's an attitude of mind which you've cultivated over the past five years. You were determined never to be tempted and that determination bred fear. It's a protective shield which, my child, I intend to pierce.'

She stared up into eyes that were both mocking and hard. Why was she not retaliating— telling him to keep out of her affairs? It could be that she was afraid she might lose the work he

had offered . . . but she rather thought there
was some other explanation for her reluctance
to begin an argument with him.

'Shall we walk,' she suggested, trying to
sound coolly civil and half-hoping he would
regard it as a snub. But he merely laughed and,
before she could even guess what he was about
she was swung into his arms and soundly kissed
on the lips.

'Oh . . . you promised—'

'Yes, my child,' he said, 'we'll walk.'

'I wish I could understand you,' she complained as she trotted beside him, keeping pace
with his long and easy strides.

'Perhaps you would, if you made the effort.'

'Your interest in me seems out of proportion.'
They were walking quickly towards the shore,
the lonely shore where palms and casuarinas
and other vegetation made a background of
dark, mysterious solitude. Clare had loved walking alone along the narrow shady paths—
walking into nowhere because they all circled
back to the shore. But now . . . Lifting her face
to glance at her companion in profile she owned
that what he had said about fear was true.

'Out of all proportion to what?' came Luke's
query at length.

'Well . . . your promise to Phil. You're going to
great lengths to honour that promise.' They had
reached the gap in the hibiscus hedge that
separated the private grounds of the hotel from
the beach, and he stopped, his hand still enclosing hers.

'I have my reasons,' he said, looking down at her with an enigmatic smile. 'I never do anything without a very good reason, Clare.'

Her heart seemed to turn a somersault; she could have eased her body close to his, lifted her lips, inviting his kiss. Warmth flowed over her and through her for surely there was no mistaking his meaning. She looked up at him, at the hovering smile, and the sensation of joy was heightened. And then without the slightest warning her mind was a whirlpool of conflicting emotions, a ferment of uncertainty and doubt as, creeping into her consciousness, memories ruthlessly obliterated her happiness.

She made to withdraw her hand but Luke's grip tightened, painfully. It was as if, because he was regarding her so intently, he had guessed at her changed emotions. She saw his mouth compress, his eyes glint like dangerous points of steel. For a moment it seemed that he struggled with his temper, as they both stood there in the moonlight and the quiet, with only night sounds to break the silence. But despite his efforts his temper broke the rein and, seizing Clare by the shoulders, he shook her unmercifully, shook her until he himself was breathless.

'Now,' he thundered, 'does that teach you a lesson!'

She swayed, her legs like jelly, her heart throbbing painfully against her ribs, and she would have fallen had he not held her, for she was overcome with fatigue, weakened by his violence. Tears ran unchecked down her cheeks and within seconds great despairing sobs were racking her body.

'Why—why d-did you do th-that?' she whispered, instinctively clinging to him for support. 'How could you? I—I hadn't done anything.'

'Only recalled those damned memories,' he rasped. 'Can't you understand that the constant re-creation of a memory must in the end become an obsession—a damned unhealthy one! How the hell is it going to end! Have you thought of that?'

She swallowed the lump that was blocking her throat. Not since the death of her fiancé had she felt so desperately unhappy. For she had just realised that she loved Luke, and it seemed very much as if he loved her.

But there was her promise . . .

'I c-can't help it if—if my memories keep on returning,' she said indignantly when she had made some attempt to stop crying. 'I've told you so many times—you don't understand.'

'You're right there! I do not understand!'

'You would if you'd loved someone, desperately, and then lost them. And if you'd made a promise to be true for ever—'

'For ever! Do you know what you're saying?'

'A promise is a promise.'

'There are circumstances when promises made in good faith can be broken. Aren't you ever going to live?'

The tears started to her eyes again, and to her astonishment he took out a handkerchief and began to dry them, infinite tenderness in the action. She still clung to his jacket, her mouth twisting in slow, convulsive movements.

'Can we go back?' she pleaded, like a child asking a favour. 'I must go back.'

The handkerchief was being put away in his pocket as she spoke. Luke shook his head at her request and said she could hardly enter the hotel looking like that.

'It's your fault!' she cried spiritedly. 'Why did you do it? You haven't answered me!'

'I lost my temper.' There was neither contrition nor regret in his voice and yet his hands were gentle on her arms. 'You goad me, Clare, by your stupidity and the rigid way you stick to that promise.'

She said nothing, nor did she make any protest when he led her through the gap and on to the beach. The sand was powder soft beneath her feet, the breeze cool and healing as it caressed her face. To her surprise she was quickly recovering from the violent scene but her heart still hammered uncomfortably against her ribs. She ventured after a while, 'Do you still want me to help you?'

'I shall be angry if you don't. You've given me your promise.' The emphasis on the last word was a deliberate jibe which brought twin spots of crimson to her cheeks.

'You're very unkind,' she complained on a quivering little sob. 'Have you no feelings at all?'

For answer he drew an exasperated breath and merely increased his pace. They fell silent for a few minutes, walking close and yet, thought Clare, a million miles apart.

But she was wrong. Once well away from any lights Luke took her hand and drew her into the shadow of the trees. She stood passive as, with a gentle hand beneath her chin, he made her look up at him. He shook his head, another gesture of exasperation.

'What must I do with you?' he sighed. 'I really don't believe a spanking would do any good, so I shall kiss you instead—'

'No I—'

'Take your pick,' he challenged darkly. 'I mean to do one or the other, Clare.'

The threat went home and with a little sigh of resignation she quivered, 'You had better kiss me, then—and I hope you enjoy it!'

'I shall, and so will you, my child,' He slid an arm about her waist, drawing her unresistingly to him, while with his free hand he lifted her face and covered her mouth with his. She sensed his affection for her; it still came through even when his demanding lips became almost brutal, his tongue forcing her lips apart to explore her mouth. A fierce pang shot through her, effectively stripping her of any resistance even when his hand slid low and its pressure arched her back to bring her body even closer, melding her to his hard and sinewed frame, compelling her to feel the virile strength that would awaken in her the dream and the desire whose meaning was total surrender. No words passed between them, but a low moan of sheer ecstasy left her lips to fire his ardour to even stronger depths. Their bodies swayed to a rhythm that matched their breathing and all the world was forgotten in the miracle of their intimacy. She felt small and meek and she had never realised it could be so rapturously pleasant. His lips moved, to find tender, vulnerable places behind her ear and along her throat. She was limp and submissive in his arms and when his hand left the middle of her back to loosen the buttons of her evening blouse her only emotion was the thrill of expectancy, the need for his touch on her bare flesh. With the ease and confidence of the expert his hand found the fastening of her bra and it was undone. He brought her breast to his mouth and she thrilled to the hardness of the nipple between his teeth. As rapture swelled within her she felt the wild surge of blood to her heart, an ecstatic flame searing her whole body, sapping her strength, affecting her sanity. His iron-hard thighs were the pleasure-pain torture that finally brought forth from her lips the plea for him to love her.

'Is that really what you want?' His voice was low, throaty with passion. 'Are you quite sure?'

The spell was broken by his words, by the implication of doubt; and she drew away, her breasts rising and falling with the intensity of her emotions.

'No,' she murmured, sanity returning. 'No, it isn't what I want.' At the apology in her tone Luke's mouth quirked. It was with relief that she saw he was not angered by her change of

mind. Somehow, he was making her feel at
ease, unembarrassed and even unashamed.
Tenderness and gratitude mingled and on sudden impulse she went up on tiptoe and kissed
him on the lips. A little laugh escaped him
before he swung her right off her feet, holding
her aloft then lowering her gently to the ground.
He looked at her and said, 'Turn around,' which
she did, and another wild thrill of rapture was a
deluge of warmth at the contact of his fingers as
they dealt with the fastening of her bra. Instead
of turning her around he left his hands inside
her blouse, sliding them down until they were
stopped by the tight waistband of her skirt. A
small laugh, good-humoured and rueful, accom-
panied the action of bringing her round to face
him.

'Shall we go back?' he suggested after a
pause. 'Phil's expecting to have a drink with us.'

She nodded, marvelling at his calm, when she
herself was having the greatest difficulty in
gaining control of her emotions.

'Yes, of course. We've been out ages.'

'Not more than half an hour.'

'It seems longer than that.'

'What prosaic talk is this?' he teased, tugging
a lock of hair that had fallen across her face.
'The time seems longer, my child, because we
did so much. Not a second was wasted.'

To her own surprise she laughed and said, 'I
don't suppose you ever do waste time.'

There was a hint of archness in her manner

which, because it lacked coquetry, was very appealing to the man at her side, and he reached down to take her hand. They walked in companionable silence back along the moonlit beach to the hotel where, after meeting Phil in the lounge and having a drink with him, Luke took his leave of them, promising to come over the following evening and have a long discussion with Clare about the new project.

Clare was at the reception desk when the woman sauntered in, the waft of heady perfume preceding her. Clare glanced up, her breath catching at the sheer beauty of the woman's features and the perfection of her figure.

'I made a reservation.' Big, widely-spaced eyes of cornflower blue travelled almost insolently over that part of Clare's body seen above the desk and she found herself bristling instantly. 'I booked a suite.'

'A suite?' echoed Clare shaking her head. 'We don't have suites here, I'm afraid.'

'Mrs Wesley—Stella Wesley! You must have a suite for me! It was booked through an agent in New York.' The fine nostrils quivered, accentuating the arrogance on the woman's face. 'Look, girl look! You haven't even opened the book!'

Clare paled with anger. 'I've no need to look in the book for a suite,' she replied. 'We have luxury rooms with private baths, and if you've booked in here it will be one of those which has been allocated to you.' She slid the book towards her and opened it. She had no recollection of making a reservation for a Mrs Stella Wesley so she assumed it must have been made before she came to work at the hotel. Yes, the name was there, and it was a deluxe room facing the sea that had been reserved for her. She looked up at the woman and said, 'We do have a room booked—'

'I demand a suite!' she interrupted rudely. 'You'll have to arrange one for me—put two or three rooms at my disposal! There are communicating doors, I presume?'

'Yes, there are, but I'm afraid we can't arrange a suite for you. There must have been some misunderstanding on the part of the travel agent—'

'All right, there was some misunderstanding. We've already established that. The remedy is for you to shake yourself and see that a suite is made available!'

Claire's chin lifted; she had taken just about as much as she could, and her voice was icily frigid as she said, 'It will be the room, Mrs Wesley, or nothing.'

The other woman's eyes opened wide. It was plain that she was not used to having her demands ignored.

'Get me the manager—at once!' she ordered, waving aside whatever Clare was going to say. 'At once,' she repeated when Clare had not moved.

'Very well.' She cast her a contemptuous

glance, swiftly taking in the perfectly-tailored suit she wore, the pure silk blouse beneath the jacket. Ears and throat and wrists were adorned with diamonds, and on the third finger of her left hand she wore a gold wedding ring and a magnificent ring of sapphires and diamonds. 'I'll fetch my brother.'

'Your brother?' with an interrogating lift of her delicately-curved eyebrows. 'Is he the manager?'

Clare nodded and turned away without answering. Her blood boiled and she could easily have told the woman to clear off as the hotel had no room for people like her, but by some supreme effort she kept a firm rein on her temper, deciding it was Phil's place to deal with this objectionable client, not hers.

She found him in his office, and immediately he saw her pallor and he asked what was wrong.

Clare explained, saw him grimace as he rose from the chair, swivelling it away from the desk as he did so.

'She's alone, yet she wants a suite?'

'Some people do, and it's their choice. I've nothing to say to that. What riled me was her attitude; anyone else, although disappointed, perhaps, at the mistake, would have been gracious about it and either taken the room or refused it. She hasn't done either. She just stood there arrogantly demanding the suite she had expected to get.'

Shrugging his shoulders, Phil went off and

Clare followed, not wanting to return to the desk but forced to do so in case she was needed by other guests. The woman glowered at her before giving her haughty attention to Phil. There was an argument, with heated words coming from Mrs Wesley and quiet, apologetic ones from Phil.

'It isn't any use your continuing to complain like this,' he said at last, still in that calm unruffled tone. 'We can't supply what we haven't got.'

The woman's mouth went tight, indicating the fury within her.

'You just won't go to any trouble!' she rasped. 'That's what it amounts to! I shall make it my business to get in touch with the owner of this hotel and make a complaint—about you both!' she said as her eyes slid to Clare.

'You can have the room,' offered Phil, ignoring her threat. 'It's reserved for you and I do assure you it's a charming room, recently redecorated and furnished. There's a settee and an easy chair, a desk, and all the other furniture necessary for your complete comfort.'

Mrs Wesley drew a loud, exasperated breath.

'How do you know what is necessary for my comfort?' she asked insolently. 'One room would stifle me!'

'It's a very large room, Mrs Wesley, and the long window opens onto a verandah which faces the hotel gardens and the sea. I assure you you won't feel stifled.'

Clare, marvelling at his patience, certainly was not so inclined. In dealing with this insufferable creature she would long ago have ordered her off the premises.

'I suppose,' said the woman at last, 'that I shall have to take it, seeing that there isn't another hotel on the island!' With an angry flounce she swung away, waving an imperious hand to the waiting porter. 'Take my luggage up!' she commanded and then, turning to Phil, 'Does he know the number?'

'It's two hundred and twenty-four.' He stood until the porter had taken the luggage to the lift before turning away and going back to his office.

'I wish she'd refused the room,' Clare was saying later when she and Phil were having afternoon tea on the patio. 'She'll be so unpleasant with the other guests, and we've such a charming crowd in this time.' Her face was troubled, her eyes clouded. 'I wonder why she came here for a holiday; it's no place for anyone on their own.'

'I must admit that has puzzled me, too. However, we have had people on their own before.'

'Not often since I came, and in any case, they've been elderly. This woman's no more than thirty—or perhaps a year or so older. I wonder why she's on her own.'

'She's devastatingly beautiful,' declared Phil, bypassing his sister's last sentence. 'I don't think I've ever seen such perfection in a woman.' He passed the muffin basket to Clare, but she shook her head.

'I've had enough, thank you, Phil.'

'Yes,' mused Phil, selecting a patty case stuffed with minced chicken and biting into it, 'extraordinarily beautiful.'

'But hard, and thoroughly detestable. I wonder what her husband's like.'

Phil gave a wry grimace.

'I don't envy him,' he said with fervour. 'I'll bet she leads him a dance!'

'Perhaps that's why she's on her own. I expect he made the excuse that he couldn't get away from the office—' She broke off, laughing, and said they were both assuming things which were in all probability wrong. 'She could be a widow,' she ended, little knowing that she had hit upon the truth.

Chapter Five

True to his word, Luke came over to the Rusty Pelican that evening. Clare, having taken extra care with her appearance, watched from the flower-draped sun-terrace as he strode across the lawn, taking a short cut from Silver Springs to enter the hotel grounds where they joined the beach. He saw her and waved; her heartstrings tugged with a pleasure-pain sensation. How she loved him! And yet memories and promises had intruded again. Yes, from waking this morning to bright sunshine pouring into her room until now, the promise she had made to Frank's mother had continually intruded. What must she do? Her own resolve to be true to the memory of her dead fiancé was weakening with every meeting with Luke, and yet there were moments when Frank's face was clear before her mind and then all her love for him seemed to well up and she felt sure no one could ever take his place. To be married to one man and thinking of another . . . It would be sheer hell, trying to deceive her husband.

Her husband. . . . As yet Luke had made no mention of love, so marriage was obviously not yet in his mind. It was even possible that he did not love her at all, that he merely wanted to succeed in making her forget the past and learn to live again. Or he could possibly be interested in her only as a potential mistress. The thought was too painful and she thrust it from her mind. In any case, Luke was close, his majestic strides bringing him to the terrace where several groups of guests were relaxing in loungers or sitting at white wrought-iron tables drinking iced lemonade through long straws, chatting, enjoying the cool evening breeze wafting in from the crystal clear sea.

'I'm early,' stated Luke after a cordial greeting and a long appreciative examination of her face and figure, and the dress of white lace she was wearing over a copper-rose underskirt. Ankle-length, with a full flowing skirt, nipped in waist and tight bodice—sleeveless and low-cut—it suited her to perfection, accentuating her adorable curves and contrasting most attractively with the honey-peach tone of her skin. 'I thought we could have a little preliminary chat over drinks.' He stood, towering over her, his oyster-coloured linen suit superlatively cut to fit his equally superlative frame. Clare's eyes wandered over him, and she thought that he could not be carrying an ounce of excess weight. But the slender body was deceptive, as she had already learned, having experienced his powerful animal strength, the coiled-spring hardness of his body. It must be all muscle, she thought. 'What, child, are you thinking?' A hint of amusement in his voice and a glimmer in his eyes. She coloured a little but her fluttering smile was impish.

'My thoughts are secret,' she told him archly. 'Mind your own business.'

'My girl,' he said warningly, 'everything you do is my business, and don't you forget it.'

She laughed, a happy, tinkling laugh that set that nerve pulsating in his throat. He bent to whisper softly in her ear, 'If it wasn't for all these people I'd kiss you! Where can we go? There are times in one's life when the presence of others is definitely unnecessary!' His eyes were dancing and a quirk of amusement lifted the corners of his mouth.

'If it's a drink you want,' she returned mischievously, 'then we could sit here. Or perhaps you prefer the lounge?'

The grey eyes glinted, but the smile still lingered as he said, giving her hair a tug, 'Evasion will get you nowhere. I thought you knew me better than to try that.'

'But you did say you wanted to chat over drinks,' she countered, feigned innocence in her glance. 'Er—have you changed your mind?'

'No, he answered. 'I haven't changed my mind. Drinks and talk it is.'

'Oh. . . .' Taken aback by his words, Clare forgot her pose, staring at him in comical dismay. He gave a gust of laughter, regarding in some amusement the rising colour in her cheeks.

'How very transparent you are! It serves you right if you've missed a special treat; you asked for it!'

'Treat? What an opinion you have of yourself! I wouldn't care if you never kissed me again!'

'You little liar,' he returned softly. And then, taking her arm. 'Come on if we're to have that drink. I want to tell you what's happening on Windward Cay.'

A few moments later they were in the lounge, tucked away at a table for two behind some potted palms, and after ordering the drinks he began to outline his plans for the development of the island he had bought. The building plans were, for the most part, no problem, as at one time the two families had themselves decided to develop and in consequence plans for two hotels had been passed already.

'They soon realised that they hadn't sufficient money,' Luke continued, 'and so the idea was dropped. However, to have plans already passed is a great advantage as work can begin almost immediately.'

'Are the plans what you want?' she asked, feeling sure they were not. 'I mean, their ideas would be vastly different from yours, wouldn't they?'

'Yes, but it's far easier to alter than to start from scratch, mainly because then it takes time to get the plans passed. I've studied them carefully and although the alterations will be major ones, they're mainly internal, so it should not be any problem to get the actual building under way without much delay at all.' He was brisk, enthusiastic, his eyes faraway. 'Additions externally can come later. For the present I shall be satisfied with the sizes of both hotels as I'd like to get them ready for next season.

'Next season?' blinked Clare. 'But that's only about nine months away!'

'What of it? With enough workers it's possible.'

'You know better than I, Luke, but it seems a very short time to me.'

'I shall submit the plans for the third hotel as soon as I've thought them out and had them drawn up,' he decided, bypassing what she had said. 'But of course that one will not be built until next year, or perhaps the beginning of the

following year. However, I must get you a plan
of the first hotel so that you can begin buying
what you want. We bring in most of our require-
ments from Miami, but you already know that.
You'll have to order everything soon, so as to be
sure to get them here in time.'

'I hope I won't let you down, Luke.'

He smiled at her from above the rim of his
glass.

'Have confidence in yourself, Clare,' he advised, 'for I have plenty in you.'

'You're very . . . kind.'

He laughed and reminded her that she had not
always thought so.

'I seem to remember you calling me a beast,'
he added on a teasing note.

'Well, you did ask for it!'

'I was only trying to teach you something.' He
paused as if unsure of himself, a circumstance
which staggered Clare, who would never have
believed he would ever be without that innate
confidence that had struck her from the very
first. 'Have I taught you anything?' he queried at
last.

The question took her unawares and she
floundered, saying, before she quite knew it, 'I
don't know, Luke. I can't say. Sometimes—' She
stopped, not knowing just how to put into words
what was in her mind. Luke did it for her, with
ruthless bluntness, his voice hardening, his eyes
cold as steel.

'So we're back to memories again. You're the
most infuriating woman I have ever met!' he

exploded, making her give a start that set her pulses racing. 'Your warped ideas are positively unhealthy—!'

'Luke,' she broke in unhappily, 'you haven't given me time to speak—'

'You didn't know what to say. Admit it.'

'You're right, I didn't.' She swallowed hard, trying to clear her throat of the blockage that was making speech so difficult. 'It isn't easy to change one's ideas—' She broke off and spread her hands. 'I loved Frank desperately—you have no knowledge of how it is to lose someone so very dear to you.' She stopped again as he uttered a muffled oath. Of a surety his temper was giving him trouble, and Clare felt righteously indignant because she had certainly not given him an excuse for being as angry as this. His impatience with her she could understand, but anger of this strength she could not. He ought to give her time, show a little patience, try to understand her feelings and her doubts. 'I said just now that you're kind,' she went on perseveringly, 'but sometimes you're hard and unfeeling. . . .' Her voice trailed as, through a gap in the greenery, she perceived the tall svelte figure of Stella Wesley entering the lounge. Luke, puzzled by her expression, twisted his head, then gave an exclamation of disbelief.

'Stella,' he muttered to himself, appearing to have forgotten Clare's presence. 'What is she doing here?'

'You know her?' Something decidedly unpleas-

ant caught at Clare's throat as an inexplicable
sense of foreboding flooded over her.

'I used to be engaged to her.' Luke spoke
automatically, scarcely able to take his eyes off
the incredibly beautiful woman who was gliding
along the middle of the lounge, glancing about
her as if looking for someone.

'Engaged? She's the one—the girl who—'

'Yes. We were madly in love once.' His voice
was harsh, grating on Clare's ears. 'She married
someone else, and now she's widowed.'

A quivering hand went to Clare's cheek.
Widowed . . . And she was here, on Flamingo
Cay. Did she know that Luke was living here? It
seemed likely. . . .

'How long has she been widowed?' she asked,
her eyes on the girl who was still scanning the
people sitting in the lounge.

'About six months.' He too was watching the
girl, and his tone had an absent ring as he
answered Clare's question. 'Perhaps a little
less.'

'That's not long.' It seemed that he had not
heard because he made no reply, and after a
moment Clare added quietly, 'Did she know you
were living here? I mean—you haven't always
lived here—' She stopped and began again. 'You
weren't living here when you were engaged,
were you?'

'No.'

'How long ago was it that you and she were
engaged?' The girl had stopped; a waiter came

to her, indicating a table and after a slight
hesitation she accepted the chair he had pulled
out for her. How beautiful and poised. Every
head had turned as she walked down the middle
of the lounge and even now, when she was
seated, people were looking at her.

'How long?' Luke sounded impatient, she
thought, and he did not even look at her as he
replied, 'Six years. She's not changed a bit.' He
was talking to himself, a vacant air about him.

Clare picked up her glass, a terrible weight
dragging at her heart. Stella was so devastatingly lovely, exquisite in her feminine perfection.
And yet, if Luke had wanted to take up with her
again he would have been in touch with her
before now, since he obviously had known that
she was a widow.

'Are—are you going to speak to her?' she could
not help asking, placing her glass down on the
table without putting it to her lips.

'Not at the moment.' His attention came back
to Clare and he smiled, obviously having forgotten what they were talking about before his
mind was diverted by the unexpected appearance of his old flame. 'Drink up and we'll go in to
dinner.'

She took up her glass, much of the weight
lifting from her heart. She had been so sure that
Luke would want to talk to Stella but, judging
from his expression at this moment, he did not
appear to have the least interest in talking to
her.

Phil was not at the table and a short while

after they had been seated a waiter came with the message that he was busy and would probably have his meal in his office. Clare did not know whether to be glad or sorry. It was always a pleasure to have the evening meal with her brother . . . but it was an even greater pleasure to be dining alone with Luke.

They chose Bahamian food, fish—grouper for Clare and bone-fish for Luke—topping the list as a natural choice, being the *specialité de la maison,* cooked as it always was, native style in a variety of intriguing ways. A fruity white wine went well with both and after having coffee at the table they got up to leave, Luke suggesting they go along to the Clipper Inn and have a planter's punch. All the time they were eating Clare's eyes had scanned the tables but there was no sign of Mrs Wesley. She must be having dinner in her room, Clare decided, wondering if Luke had been thinking of her and concluding—as she had done—that Stella was dining in her room.

Over drinks in the Clipper Inn Luke talked some more about the development of the island and as she listened Clare realised more and more that there was something idyllic in his plan. He was intent on creating a little piece of paradise on one of the Out Islands and she felt proud that she was to play such an active part in that creation. Her mind buzzed with ideas for colour schemes, materials, furnishings, ornaments and so much more. Luke began talking about the outside, the smooth lawns, the flower beds, the flood-lit tennis courts set in a palm grove with exotic flowers trailing along the border wall. The golf-course of one hotel was to be between a lake and the sea, and dotted with palms and other exotic trees.

'It all sounds so exciting that I can't wait to see it finished!' she declared, her eyes aglow with enthusiasm. 'How long will it be before I'm actually able to begin?'

'The inside, you mean? About six or seven months. But you've a lot to do before then,' he warned. 'Everything must be here, on this island, ready to be put in place once the builders are out.'

'I know.' She paused, hesitant about her next question even while knowing it had to be asked. 'The expenses, Luke . . . Shall I have to come to you for every cent? It would be easier if—'

'I shall place a sum of money at your disposal,' he interrupted quietly. 'You'll be able to sign cheques when necessary. I'll give you a list of some of the best places in Miami to buy such things as drapes and rugs and furniture. You'll be buying wholesale at places that cater exclusively to hotels.' He talked for a few more minutes before suggesting they take a stroll. Clare looked at him, desiring nothing more than to be with him in the romantic setting of the beach, and the secluded little groves that lay so temptingly behind it, the palm trees along their borders waving their spidery fronds against the deep purple sky of a Bahamian night. But she was reluctant at the same time, aware of what would happen, aware of the temptation Luke would put in her way. It was not that he wanted to seduce her—on the contrary. He did, though, want to make her forget, open her arms to the future instead of clinging to the past. As she had told him several times, he did not understand. Until she had met Luke it had been easy to keep faith, and although she no longer resented the power Luke had to make her forget, she was by no means sure she wanted to forget totally. So it was better to keep to her resolve and avoid temptation. She turned to him and said she was too tired.

'Another time,' she promised. 'It's very late, anyway.'

'Half past ten,' he said, glancing at his watch. 'It's early, child, not late.' His glance was both shrewd and sardonic. 'Scared again. I'll not take any more,' he went on imperiously. 'You'll come outside with me.'

'Luke—' Her face was strained. 'I'd rather not, if you don't mind.'

'I do mind! I intend to wear you down, Clare, so you might just as well give in now.'

'I don't understand you,' she sighed. 'I know I've said it before—'

'Several times, and no doubt you will again.' His deep male voice held an odd inflection as he added, 'You'll understand well enough in time—when I'm ready to explain.'

'Can't you explain now?' she pleaded, then

blushed hotly, for she saw by his changed expression that he knew she was asking him to say he loved her.

Yes, she was asking him to say he loved her even though at the back of her mind she realised that it would cast her into wild confusion, simply because she had not reached the point where, should he ask her to marry him, she could gladly say yes. She cast him a speculative glance and guessed without any doubt at all that he knew she was not ready, hence his words, '. . . when I am ready to explain.' It meant of course that as soon as he could be sure of the answer he wanted, he would tell her he loved her and ask her to marry him.

'Shall we go outside?' he suggested, changing the subject. 'I'm not intending to accept a refusal, Clare,' he warned. 'Let's go.'

So persevering in his object, and patient . . . sometimes! She hoped he would never get the idea that she was playing hard to get.

He had risen; his stern regard was a challenge and she got up from her chair, following meekly when he led the way from the bar to the sun terrace and then into the hotel grounds. The fountains played in the moonlight—silver rain tinted with rose and green and gold from the lamps fixed to the drooping branches of the casuarina trees. There was no sound other than their cascading music and the mysterious, rhythmic beat of a goombay drum drifting across from some place in the far distance—a native village, perhaps. All was magic, with the high argent moon shedding its gentle light on the grounds of the hotel, on the low hills behind and the dark expanse of sea in front, painting the tiny wavelets with silver.

Luke reached for her hand, a sort of arrogant possessiveness in the action. Clare glanced up at him, at that handsome profile, and her heart was light. She loved him so what else mattered in the whole wide world? Why was she keeping him in suspense, often exasperating him with her capriciousness? She might lose him if she went on like this much longer, she thought, fear ripping through her so that she wanted to blurt out the words that would bring her indecision to an end. But instead she said casually, 'Are we going far, Luke? My sandals are high-heeled, you know.'

'Then you can take them off when we reach the shore. You'll like the sand between your toes.' And when they had passed through the gap in the hibiscus hedge he told her to lift one foot so that he could take off the sandal for her. His cool fingers curled round her ankle, sending delicious ripples along her spine. The contact of his flesh was always an exciting experience, no matter where he touched her.

'The other one.' She obeyed, lifting her right foot.

'Thank you,' she murmured shyly, her slender seductive body swaying against him as she regained her balance. He caught her to him, dropping the shoes, and his mouth covered hers in a long and passionate kiss. One hand caressed her curves through the lace of her dress, persisting until the hardness of desire was wakened as the nipple shaped itself between his finger and thumb. Her breath seemed to stop for one ecstatic moment that transported her to the heights of bliss, every nerve and cell of her being set on fire by the exploration of his other hand as it progressed with slow deliberation towards her thigh. A body-twisting spasm shot through her and the blood pounded in her temples.

'Luke . . .' His name rose from the depths of her throat like a sob behind tears. 'Please—' The rest was stemmed by his full, sensuous mouth enclosing hers with brutal force as all his primitive instincts quickened, brought to full vigour by the warmth of her pliant body straining against his male hardness. Her arms were around him, inside his jacket; she felt the leanness of his frame, knew the undiluted ecstasy of his heart throbbing in wild disorder against her breast.

'Clare,' he groaned, crushing her mouth even as the name escaped his lips. The heady tang of sandalwood after-shave, the faintly pungent smell of freshly-laundered linen stirred Clare's senses equally as much as the musky male odour that had assailed her nostrils from the start.

For a long long time their bodies swayed in unison as, wrapped in the magic of their own ecstatic world they were carried to the heights of heaven by the intensity of their erotic emotions.

But at last Luke drew away, a low laugh escaping from lips that were warm from her kisses.

'I wonder if you know just what you do to me?' His hands gripped her waist, warm and tender and possessive. 'You have no inhibitions at times like this . . . but what will you be like tomorrow when in the cold light of day you review your conduct of tonight?' Serious the tone and carrying a distinct note of anxiety not unmingled with a trace of anger. 'Shall I find my maid reluctant again as memories warp her judgement?'

Clare, her body still limp from his love-making, had no desire to talk of such things. On the contrary, she was ready and willing for him to make love to her again. But as she looked up into his finely-chiselled features she knew for sure that he was no longer in a reciprocal mood. He had won again but was wondering what tomorrow would bring. It was natural that he should, natural too that he considered her not only to be obstinate but inconsistent as well, love for him carrying her away from memories at one moment, and love for a man who was dead bringing her back the next.

'Have patience with me, Luke,' she pleaded, pressing her face into his shirt and uttering a long-drawn-out sigh that was almost a sob. 'It's all so new, and it's happened so unexpectedly—'

'It was bound to happen one day,' he broke in hardily. 'If it hadn't been me it would certainly have been someone else.'

She did not agree, for she was convinced that

if she had not met Luke then no other man
would ever have attracted her. He was something special in every way, a man in a million,
and as she dwelt on the fact that he had chosen
her from all other women, she declared it to be a
miracle.

Another shuddering sigh issued from her lips
as she felt him stir with impatience. Had he
expected that tonight he would break down her
defences completely, win from her lips a confes-
sion of love, making it easy for him to declare his
love and then ask her to marry him? Usually it
was the man who first declared his love but this
situation was different. It was understandable
that he was holding back until he could be sure
of her answer being what he desired. No man
wants the humiliation of a refusal to his proposal of marriage—especially a man with Luke
Mortimer's pride and arrogance.

She spoke, softly and pleadingly, asking again
to be given time. 'Don't be angry,' she begged
when with an abrupt, exasperated movement he
put her from him, his hands hardening around
her flesh as he did so. He looked almost savage
and she sensed that nothing would give him
greater satisfaction than to beat her—to knock
some sense into her, as he had once put it.
Instead, he spoke harshly to her, telling her it
was time they went back to the hotel.

'I've got to be up early in the morning,' he
snapped as a final sentence, before total silence
fell between them. A curt goodnight was all

Luke said by way of breaking that silence and Clare, tears welling up in her eyes, turned and went into the hotel without being able to answer him.

Chapter Six

There had been a sudden thunderstorm and the earth and atmosphere were fresh with rain. Clare, who invariably spent part of her lunch hour in the gardens, strolled along paths of newly-washed gravel towards the copse of bamboo palms beside which was a little rustic seat. It was wet still, even though the sun was in the sky again and everything was drying out under its heat. She walked on, then stopped to watch a tiny humming-bird hovering over a flower, searching for nectar. She was depressed, and there was a persistent little pulsing of pain in her temples, the result of anxiety because of the change that had come over Luke last night. He had been almost hostile towards her, and it certainly did not help to know that it was all her own fault. He would become so impatient with her in the end that he would probably decide to abandon his attempts and let her continue to live on her memories. If only he could understand the nerve-twisting agony of her indecision, then perhaps he would have patience, give her time. But she suspected that, the way he was feeling at present, his impatience stemmed mainly from desire for her.

She sighed and walked on, her eyes on the shore where a bronzed young giant was playing beach ball with two young children, a boy and a girl. Their laughter rang out and a yearning awoke within Clare's heart. To have a family, reaping all the pleasures that it could give, to gain the status of a mother. Was there any need for all that to be lost to her? For the entire morning she had found Luke's manner preying on her mind, creating fear . . . fear that he would lose interest in her.

She would have to surrender, she had concluded, not only because of his indomitable determination to break her to his will, but because of her own feelings, the love she had for him, the way he drew her both physically and mentally. They had much in common in every way—a love of beauty and of peace, an idealism which could be both exciting and fulfilling, were they to continue through life doing things together in the way they were to do things on his newly-acquired little island, Windward Cay, one of the hundreds of Out Islands scattered like leaves over the sparkling, emerald-green waters of the Atlantic Ocean.

Still strolling on, Clare found herself by the gap in the hedge and stood for a moment, undecided as to whether she had time for a short walk along the beach. She decided against it and turned to retrace her steps back to the hotel, her mind still absorbed by her problem. But it was becoming less troublesome with every hour that passed, because her mind was almost made up— Her thoughts braked as she heard her name called by Mary, who had relieved her during the lunch hour. 'You're wanted on the phone, Clare,' she said from a short distance, 'Mr Mortimer.'

Luke . . . What did he want at this time of the day? Clare's legs became like jelly as the conviction swept through her that he was calling to tell her he did not want her services after all. He had had enough of her; he had decided to get some-one else. She found herself trying to run but was held back by a dragging weight and the sensa-tion of fatigue brought on by her heart hammer-ing with wild intensity against her ribs. She was breathing hard by the time she reached the phone, fear mounting out of all proportion as her conviction was strengthened, and when she picked up the receiver she waited in an agony of suspense for the words she felt sure would come.

'Hello, Clare. Feeling any better this morn-ing?' His tone suggested a hint of mocking amusement as he added, before giving her time to speak, 'You sound breathless. It's gratifying to know that you come running at my command.'

'You—!' She had sagged with relief at his first

words, but now she stiffened, anger bringing
bright spots of colour to cheeks that had been
pearl-white. 'What an opinion you have of yourself! I've *not* been running. Sorry to disappoint
you!'

'You don't sound sorry,' he laughed. 'What
made you breathless then—anxiety in case I had
rung to say I was casting you off?'

Gasping at his perception she had nothing to
say in answer to the question, so she changed
the subject, managing to sound casual as she
asked him why he had rung.

'To stop you worrying,' he replied, taking her
off balance. 'I'm not thinking of throwing in the
towel any more than you are of telling me, once
and for all, to go to the devil.' So cool the voice
but tinged with ironic humour not unmingled
with censure. 'I knew you'd be worrying, because you're an idiot, and I did have a mind to
phone you earlier, but decided it would do you no
harm to be left in suspense for a while. It might
prove to be effective.'

Clare held the receiver from her, staring at it
and wondering whether to hang up on Luke or
reveal just what was in her heart. She did
neither, but merely made an objection to being
called an idiot. 'If that's what you think,' she
continued tartly, 'then why are you wanting me
to help you?'

'Ah, you have me stumped there,' was his surprising admission. 'You must be a rather special
kind of idiot; there's no other explanation that
I can think of on the spur of the moment.'

She found herself laughing heartily. 'Luke,' she said, 'you're incorrigible!'

'So we're happy again?' His voice changed dramatically and he was serious. She knew that by 'we' he had meant her alone. She said softly, almost tenderly, 'Yes, Luke, I'm happy again.'

'Stay that way, my sweet. See you this evening in the nautical atmosphere of the Tavern Restaurant of the Rusty Pelican. So long for now.'

'So long. . . .' He had hung up already. She smiled into the receiver as she replaced it on its rest. Her doubts had all dissolved and she knew what she wanted to do. A warm glow of well-being infused her as the decision was made. Tonight she would find a way of telling Luke what was in her heart.

She stared at the envelope for a long while before slitting it open. The letter from Mrs Weedall had arrived a few minutes ago, having come by the mail boat from Nassau. Clare's fingers trembled as she slit the envelope and withdrew the single sheet of paper.

'My dear Clare,' she read, 'I am so desolate these days without seeing you and talking as we used to do about my darling Frank. And so I am accepting the invitation you so kindly sent me and I'm coming over to visit you. Will Phil let you have a holiday? We could chat and be together and reminisce about those happy days before the tragedy that spoiled both our lives. I made up my mind suddenly, because I was so miserable, here on my own in this house, and I

shall be with you on Wednesday the tenth,
having been lucky enough to get a seat on a
plane going to Miami. From there I fly to Flamingo Cay, and it takes only about twenty
minutes. I believe it is the off-season period in
the Bahamas, and, therefore, I expect Phil will
find me a room without any trouble, but please
apologise to him for my coming over without
giving more notice.' There followed the num-
bers and times of the flights and then Mrs
Weedall ended with all her love.

The paper fluttered in Clare's trembling fingers. Everything had come bursting back upon
her, Frank's image totally obliterating that of
Luke. Guilt poured over her in a deluge of shame
as she thought of the promise she had so solemn-
ly made to the woman who was coming out here
with the expectation of being comforted. How
could she, Clare, have faced Mrs Weedall if she
had pledged herself to Luke? And yet, cried her
anguished heart, how could she give Luke up
now? She was back to that state of indecision,
plunged into it by the contents of the letter she
held.

Tears welled up and rolled unchecked down
her cheeks. Turmoil raged within her, mingling
with guilt and remorse, and pity for the woman
who was coming.

The tenth . . . and it was the seventh
today. . . .

When Luke arrived he saw that something
was seriously wrong. Clare was on the sun

terrace, her eyes dark pools of anguished indecision. She could not visualise life without Luke and yet, on the other hand, she could not see herself callously informing Mrs Weedall that she was breaking her promise and marrying someone else.

'What's happened?' Luke's voice was gentle, his dark eyes troubled. 'You look shattered. Have you had bad news from home?'

Dumbly she shook her head and turned away, tears filling her eyes. There was no one on the terrace; most of the guests were already in the restaurant, while the others were probably in the lounge, drinking cocktails before dinner. Luke took Clare's face in his hand, forcing her round to look at him. 'Tell me what's wrong, my dear. I've a right to know.'

A right . . . Yes, he had a right, because he loved her and she loved him, and yet she shook her head, lifting a trembling hand to wipe away a tear that had fallen onto her cheek.

'No, Luke—'

'I do have a right,' he broke in gently, 'and you know it.' Soft the voice, but firm and authoritative. His arm slipped about her waist, bringing her slim, seductive body close up against him. 'Do you want to sit down and talk?' he asked.

'No—' She twisted in his hold, staring right into his eyes. 'Luke—I've had a letter, from Frank's mother—' She stopped as he drew a sharp breath that sounded almost like a hiss. 'She's coming for a visit—'

'Coming here!' he cut in wrathfully. 'For what reason, might I ask?'

Clare swallowed, moving out of his hold. Her face was tight and strained, devoid of colour. She was being torn to shreds by the thought of what this night might have been if she had never received that letter. 'She's a very lonely woman, Luke, and she wants to come to see me—you can't begin to know just how unhappy she is,' added Clare hastily as she saw his mouth compress. 'I wrote to her soon after I arrived here and invited her to come over whenever she felt like it. She's taken me up on the invitation and—and she'll be arriving in three days' time.'

Luke regarded her fixedly. 'Do you want her to come, Clare?' he asked.

'I—she's so lonely, and her other son's not very sympathetic, whereas I can—'

'Let her weep on your shoulder, I suppose,' he broke in with a sort of vicious sarcasm. His eyes smouldered as he added, 'You haven't answered my question: do you want her to come?'

'It'll do her good to have the change,' she began when once more Luke interrupted to remind her that she had not answered his question. 'It's difficult,' she admitted, pressing a hand unconsciously to the ache in her heart. 'I feel it's my duty to try to help her—oh, Luke, don't be angry!' she begged. 'I can't bear any more!'

'Nor can I,' he returned explosively. 'My patience is just about at an end!'

'Shall—shall we go in to—to dinner?' she

quavered, and then to her utter dismay she started to cry, weeping into her hands, her shoulders heaving with the sobs which rose from the very heart of her.

For a long moment Luke seemed immune to her suffering, lost as he was in anger, but suddenly his arms were about her, bringing her close in a tender, gentle embrace. 'Little girl,' he murmured, his cool lips caressing her temple, 'don't cry. We'll sort something out.'

She leant away, eyeing him suspiciously through her tears. 'What do you mean by that?' she queried, frowning. 'There isn't anything to sort out that I can see.'

'I'm not having that woman transmitting her misery to you at this time, Clare, so, as I said, we'll sort something out.'

'I still don't understand you—' She stopped because, having brought forth his handkerchief, he had begun to dry her cheeks. His eyes were fixed on hers, looking deeply into them, half in tenderness but half in anger. 'I don't want you to be unkind to her, Luke.'

He drew an impatient breath and after a moment asked what Phil thought about the coming visit of Mrs Weedall.

'I haven't told him yet,' she admitted. 'I know he won't be pleased, though.'

'That's an understatement. He'll be damned furious about it.'

'Yes—but he'll make her welcome just the same. Phil's like that—kind and considerate of other people's feelings.'

'If by that you mean I am not considerate, then you're quite right—where that particular woman is concerned! Phil told me your father had said she was the bane of your life when you were in England and I agree! But mark this,'— he wagged a warning, imperious finger close to her face—'she'll not be the bane of your life here. Do you understand?'

'I shall not have her upset, Luke!' she stated emphatically and heard him grit his teeth.

'Let's go in to dinner,' he snapped. 'We'll both feel better when we've eaten.' Plainly he was furious at the news she had given him, and Clare was troubled by his thoughtful expression, and also by his statement just now that they would sort something out. What had he in mind? His face, hard-masked, was half turned from her and there was a determination about it that made her doubly suspicious.

'You're not to talk to her about us,' she blurted out impulsively as the thought occurred to her that he might just take it upon himself to inform Mrs Weedall that he and Clare were keeping company and that they would probably marry. Yes, he would be quite capable of an action like that even though marriage had never yet been mentioned.

'Us?' He turned again and looked down into her tear-stained face. 'What would I say about us?' The ironic light in his eyes carried the message: he was telling her that, at present, there was nothing he could say about them. Her heart felt even heavier than before as she ac-

cepted the fact that she had taken much for
granted, founding her assumptions entirely on
the way Luke acted with her, optimistically
believing that as soon as she was willing to put
the past behind her, he would declare his love
and ask her to marry him. Perhaps, she thought
dismally, she had been too sure of herself, and of
the attraction she had for him. As if to bring her
spirits even lower, Luke was saying with slow
deliberation, 'There isn't anything I can say
about us, is there?'

Dumbly she shook her head, tears starting to
her eyes again. He took her arm and they went
towards the restaurant, but, aware of her appearance, she left him just outside the door,
saying she wanted to go to the rest room to dab
water on her eyes, and to tidy her hair. 'I look
awful,' she quivered, 'with—with crying like
that.'

He merely nodded and said he would wait just
inside the door. She went off, dismayed by the
redness of her eyes which, she realised, could
not be remedied merely by dabbing them with
water. However, the lighting in the restaurant
was very low—just candles on the tables and a
few ship's lamps on the walls—so perhaps she
would not feel any embarrassment after all, she
thought, as she dried her eyes with a tissue. A
comb through her hair, an application of the
blusher to take away the pallor of her cheeks,
and she was reasonably satisfied with her appearance.

She made her way back to the restaurant and

was about to enter when she heard Luke's voice and she stopped in her tracks, aware that he was talking to Stella Wesley.

'You're here for a few weeks, you say?'

'I need the rest and change, Luke.' Her voice was husky and low and, to Clare's critical ears, sensuously enticing. 'I arrived yesterday but had to keep to my room until now, as I was feeling off-colour.'

Clare, conscious of the head waiter glancing her way, walked forward to stand by Luke's side. Stella's eyes widened, swept her figure arrogantly, then returned to Luke. It was plain that she expected Clare to pass on, and Clare could not help the little tug of satisfaction she felt when Luke introduced her to Stella as a friend. The girl's eyes examined Clare again, this time with more interest, and also with undisguised dislike.

'I understood that Miss Winter was the receptionist here?' said Stella, arching her neck in the most attractive way as she transferred her attention to Luke.

'That's right. Clare works for her brother, Phil, who's the manager here.' He paused a moment and Clare thought that it was just like a man not to have spotted the tenseness in the atmosphere, the antagonism existing between the two young women. He calmly invited Stella to dine with them, smilingly informing her that Phil would probably be joining them in a few minutes time.

'I'd love to join you,' purred Stella, putting a

hand possessively on his arm. 'How very nice to have company when I'd been expecting to be on my own.'

Clare threw her a suspicious glance. She was convinced that Stella had come to Flamingo Cay for no other purpose than to get in touch with Luke again.

Phil arrived as they sat down at the table by the window, and stood for a moment looking from Stella to Clare, and then his eyes settled questioningly on Luke. Luke made the introductions, and if he now noticed anything strange in the atmosphere he gave no outward sign of it. Phil was politeness itself and during dinner he made it his business to ensure that Stella had all she wanted, and at one time, remembering that she had been in her room all day, he inquired with a smile, 'Are you fully recovered, Mrs Wesley? We were all very concerned that you should be starting your holiday in that way.' His eyes flicked to Clare, who had not known that Stella had spent the day in her room. She had been unusually busy at the desk, a cruise ship having come in, bringing several hundred passengers to the island for a few hours' stay and some of them, deciding they would like to take a vacation here, had come into the hotel to make reservations for the coming season.

'Yes, thank you, I'm fully recovered.' She smiled at him and no one would ever have believed that she had insulted him over and over again yesterday, ending up by threatening to report him, and his sister, to the owner of the hotel. 'I think perhaps I ate something that didn't agree with me.'

'Well, we hope you will not have that trouble here,' he returned pleasantly. 'We pride ourselves on the quality of our food, and our chef is able to cater to the most exacting gourmet tastes.'

'I'm sure he is,' with silky-toned accents and a fluttering of long, curling lashes. 'This lobster is delicious.'

Clare exchanged glances with her brother and volumes were spoken. Luke, his attention arrested, flicked his eyes almost imperceptibly from one to another, an odd expression on his face.

On the whole, the meal was not quite so uncomfortable an experience as Clare had expected when first she had heard Luke extend the invitation to Stella. He had known that the table at which they would be was one reserved permanently for Phil and Clare, but had obviously taken it for granted that Phil would not mind, especially as the extra guest was a female, so making a foursome. He was not to know of the unpleasantness that had occurred yesterday because, quite naturally, neither Phil nor Clare had dreamt of mentioning it.

During the meal it became clear that Stella was puzzled about the relationship between Luke and Clare. He was reserved, which was only to be expected when others were present, but there were occasions when his eyes took on

an expression which would certainly not please
Stella if, as Clare had supposed, she had come
here to find her old flame in the hope that he
would be willing to pick up where they had left
off some years previously.

When the meal was over Clare was both
gratified and relieved when Luke said, a moment or two after Phil had left the table, 'If you'll
excuse us, Stella—Clare and I have to talk, and
it's private.' A smile hovered on his lips but his
eyes were iron-hard, his voice coolly impersonal.
'Good night, and I hope you'll enjoy your holiday.' He was rising as he spoke, and with a
possessive gesture he slid a hand beneath
Clare's elbow and urged her up with him. Stella,
her mouth tight, failed to keep the undertone of
anger from her voice as she said,

'Good night, Luke. Yes, I'm sure I shall enjoy
my holiday.' She rose from the chair and Luke
with his customary politeness inclined his head
as she turned and left the restaurant by a
different door from that to which he began to
lead Clare.

'We're going to Silver Springs,' he told her as
soon as they were outside. 'I've got the plans of
one of the hotels up on the wall on my study and
you ought to have a look at them. You'll see the
layout of all the principal rooms which will give
you an idea of what's wanted. I'm having another set made for you but they'll take about a week.
I thought it would be a good idea for you to get
some idea of the sizes of the bedrooms, for
instance, and the windows.' He was striding out

briskly, with Clare having to skip now and then to keep up with him. 'You don't mind coming over?'

'Not at all. . . .' Her voice trailed unaccountably and he glanced down and one corner of his mouth lifted.

'Not scared again, I hope?'

She drew a deep breath. 'Let's talk about the plans,' she suggested coolly. 'If this evening's to be spent going over them, then let us keep to that particular business—'

'Clare,' he interrupted in a very soft voice, 'be careful. I don't allow anyone to talk to me like that, especially a woman.'

'Phil said that you consider us as inferior.' She hadn't meant to say anything like that and wondered, with a little shock of surprise, how it had managed to escape.

'Not inferior, but, as the weaker sex, dependent.'

'And subservient?'

He glanced down into her eyes, a frown on his brow. 'As you say, we shall talk business, nothing more!'

The gardens of Silver Springs were steeped in moonlight as they entered, but before they reached the house translucent clouds were sailing across the sky to drift over the moon, creating a mysterious purple darkness which spread like a cloak over the gardens and wrapped itself around the two people walking there. Its effect was magical; it cast a spell over everything so

that shapes were changed and colours darkened, and even the sea appeared smoother,
motionless except where its waters flowed over
the coral reef to settle in the drowsy lagoon.
Clare, caught in the spell, trapped in the witchery of her surroundings, found herself sinking
into a state of delicious lassitude, and when
Luke stopped and took her in his arms she
pressed against him for support, bringing her
arms up to encircle his neck, making it easy for
her to find a resting place for her head in the
crook of his arm. He bent to take her lips and
every nerve in her body tingled at the contact.
Sensuous and warm, his mouth explored the
tender, vulnerable places behind her ears, teasing, tempting, creating sensations that set her
body on fire with longing for him. She felt him
lift the edge of the loose-fitting evening blouse
she wore, thrilling to the nerve-vibrating touch
as his hand found and cupped her breast and
then carressed it gently, stimulating her emotions to even greater heights until she was
consumed by a searing flame of ecstasy that
threatened to rise to a conflagration that would
deprive her of her sanity, reduce her to complete
and irrevocable surrender. Perhaps that was
what Luke was intending, for if he really was
intent on marrying her, it would be the most
effective means to the end he desired.

Quivering still beneath his persuasive touch,
Clare nevertheless was able to pull herself
away, escaping the imperious hand that would
have brought her back against his hard and

sinewed frame. She was a few paces from him, her breathing heavy, her nerves still out of control and for a few silent moments she and Luke just stared at one another, their senses becoming stirred in a very different way as, the clouds having disintegrated into wisps of swirling lace, the landscape was again flooded with moon-silver radiance that brought the trees into sharp relief against a lustrous, star-spangled sky. Magic was again unleashed upon the gardens and the fountains and the motionless dark sea, magic of a different kind from what had prevailed before, but just as effective in closing the mind to all sense of reality, and before she realised it Clare was once again held within the hawser-strong embrace of Luke's arms and his full-lipped mouth was enclosing hers in a kiss so fiercely passionate that Clare, her senses reeling, felt that every primitive trait of the savage was released, draining Luke in the end so that when at last he held her from him he swayed, like someone intoxicated. 'My God, Clare,' he breathed hoarsely, 'you're the most desirable woman I have ever met!'

She managed the ghost of a smile then looked away, the image of Frank's mother superimposing itself invidiously upon every other picture in her mind, ruthlessly dragging her back to reality, to the promise she had made . . . and broken.

Luke, perceptively aware of what was happening to her, took hold of her shoulders, his fingers iron-hard probes which, she knew, would leave ghastly bruises. She flinched and steeled herself for what was to come, but to her surprise and relief he changed his mind about the shaking he had intended giving her and instead he released her and said in a voice that was briskly devoid of all emotion, 'Come along—we were intending to devote this evening to business!' And with that he swung around on his heels and strode away, uncaring that Clare had to trot to match his pace.

Chapter Seven

It was at breakfast the following morning that Clare broke the news to her brother that Mrs Weedall was coming over to Flamingo Cay and would be arriving in two days' time. 'Can I have an hour or so off to meet her and see her settled in?' she added swiftly on seeing Phil's mouth compress. 'And can I have the car, please?'

They were on the sun-terrace and the miracle of dawn had only just unfolded, its golden lustre showering the sea and highlighting the sparkling crystal waters cascading over the reef into the lagoon. Already a couple of pleasure boats were out and as she watched, shading her eyes from the sun's bright glare, Clare saw a man in mask and flippers dive into the water, and in imagination she was down in a spectacular marine wonderland, gliding languidly through a constantly-changing maze of incredibly beautiful coral formations where—among the waving gorgonians and sea-fans—thousands of multi-coloured tropical fish moved about, often so used to the divers that they would swim right up to their masks.

'She's coming here?' For once Phil's customary calm deserted him and Clare saw to her dismay that he was angry. She had half-expected him to be, though, and there was nothing she could do about it. Even had there been time to ask Mrs Weedall to cancel the trip, Clare could never have done so. She had extended the invitation and it would have been cruel to have disappointed her. 'In two days time! I invited her, when I first wrote after I arrived here,' explained Clare. 'I don't remember mentioning it to you—'

'You certainly did *not* mention it,' he broke in, frowning darkly at her. 'If you had, I'd have refused to have her.'

Clare bit her lip, and toyed with a morsel of food on her plate. 'I'm sorry, Phil, for not asking you first. It was impulsive of me, I suppose, but Mrs Weedall had been so tragically hurt by my coming here—leaving her to look after Frank's grave all on her own—that I was filled with pity and asked her over for a visit. I've not heard from her until yesterday when I received the letter telling me she was coming on the tenth of this month.' Her voice had a melancholy sound and her eyes were apologetic as they looked into his. 'We must make her welcome, Phil,' she went on perseveringly. 'She's lonely and sad and needs this break. Have pity on her,' she begged finally, a plea that melted her brother on the instant, a smile restoring the familiar softness to his face.

'There isn't anything we could do at this late stage, anyway,' he said, 'and so we must, as you say, welcome her.'

'Can she have one of the deluxe rooms facing the sea? We have several vacant,' she added persuasively.

'All right,' he agreed. 'As you say there are several vacant.'

'And I can have time off to bring her?'

'Of course.' He fell silent, considering. 'I think we can manage to let you have a week at least of the holidays that will be due to you later.' Another pause before he said, looking up from the toast he was buttering, 'Does Luke know of her visit?'

Clare nodded her head, colouring at the memory of Luke's reaction. 'Yes; he wasn't pleased.'

'It's understandable. He's been working hard to help you forget the past and now Frank's mother's coming over to open up the wound again.' Clare had nothing to say to that and after a space Phil asked how long Mrs Weedall would be staying.

'I don't know,' she answered. 'She hasn't said.'

'Let's hope it isn't too long.'

'We can't push her off until she's ready to go,' protested Clare with a pained expression.

'No, I agree.' Phil smiled suddenly and said, 'Don't look so anxious, Clare. You know me well enough to be sure I shan't do or say anything to upset her.'

She nodded, responding to his smile, and nothing more was said on the matter until that evening when Luke came into the hotel after dinner and found both Clare and Phil drinking coffee on the patio.

'Ah, Luke,' smiled Phil, indicating a chair. 'How are things? We half expected you for dinner.'

'I was busy perusing estimates for the building project, so I just took a snack in my study.' He sat down, stretching his legs out in front of him. Dressed in a light grey linen suit with a soft, draped line to the jacket, he lent a certain elegance to what was designated as casual informality by the tailors. His burnt-sienna skin seemed even darker than usual against the gleaming whiteness of his shirt, his hair shone, immaculately clean and healthy. The narrowed smile hovering on his lips revealed equally healthy teeth, pearl-white and even. Clare's senses stirred as usual and she frowned inwardly and wished it were possible to secure complete control over one's emotions. But owing to some unfathomable caprice of nature emotions danced to their own particular tune and there was no rein by which they could be held in check. She felt his eyes upon her and glanced up, but before either of them had time to speak Phil was asking Luke what he was having to drink.

'I'll have a brandy,' he said, falling silent until Phil got up and went inside to find a waiter. 'How long is this woman staying?' he inquired, a strange impenetrable air about him that both puzzled and disturbed her. She recalled fleetingly the events of last night, the atmosphere of camaraderie that had come to them after they had entered his home. He had shown her the plans, appearing to have forgotten all that had gone before, especially his anger at her change of mood. He had slipped an arm about her waist as they stood examining the large drawing on the wall; he had discussed with her at some length what he required, had warned her of likely pitfalls and finally told her not to become disheartened when snags occurred. They were bound to, he warned her, and she herself would make mistakes, but she was not to worry because mistakes, tackled properly, could almost always be put right. Yes, it had been a pleasant and friendly interlude and when eventually Luke had walked her back to the Rusty Pelican, she was feeling far happier than she would have believed possible a couple of hours earlier. Luke broke into her train of thought, inquiring again how long Mrs Weedall was staying on the island.

'I don't know,' she replied. 'Phil asked me the same thing this morning when I told him of Mrs Weedall's visit.'

'How did he take it?' asked Luke interestedly.

'He accepted it.' She broke off as his eyebrows lifted, reminding her she was evading a direct answer. 'He didn't like the idea any more than you do,' she admitted with a sigh, 'but he did at least promise not to do or say anything that would upset her.' She looked at him levelly, a challenge in her eyes.

'You're afraid that I might do or say something to upset her?'

'I don't know. . . . I'm not sure, Luke, because you're so unpredictable.'

'Unpredictable!' he echoed. 'I like that—coming from you!'

She had the grace to blush, a circumstance which afforded him immense satisfaction.

'I've a good reason for changing my mind from time to time,' she just had to point out, but before she could expand on that he was interrupting her.

'There's no tenable explanation for your attitude, Clare, so don't try to make excuses for yourself.'

'You've no patience,' she complained. 'But let's get back to Mrs Weedall. You did say that there was nothing you could tell her about us, and in my opinion that's tantamount to a promise not to upset her in any way at all.'

'It might be a promise in your opinion, but it isn't in mine, and if you suppose I'm intending to go out of my way to be pleasant to this woman then you're mistaken. I detest her even before I've met her!'

'You won't when you do meet her,' she assured
him. 'You'll pity her, in fact.'

'That,' he said shortly, 'is a matter of extreme
doubt!'

'It's a beautiful evening,' she said, deliberately changing the subject. The majestic moon was
rising over the water, and a cool sundown
breeze wafted across the garden to fan her
cheeks. 'I do love it here.'

'Well, that's something. There was a time
when I felt you would decide to leave.' His smile
taunted as he added, just as if he had to, 'It soon
became obvious, though, that you couldn't bear
the "sweet sorrow" of parting from me.'

She gasped, and it was several seconds before
she could articulate words. 'What an inflated
opinion you have of yourself!' she exclaimed,
sending him a scathing glance. 'That wasn't the
reason at all!'

'Liar,' he accused, and suddenly his voice was
soft. 'You can neither fool yourself nor me, Clare,
and you know it.'

She coloured faintly and looked away, her eyes
wandering in the direction of the Clipper Inn as
the sound of calypso music drifted out over the
sweetly perfumed air. His meaning could not
possibly elude her and there was no doubt in her
mind that if she were to steer the conversation
in the right direction the finale would be a
declaration of love on Luke's part followed by a
proposal of marriage.

But what of Mrs Weedall? Clare could think of
nothing more devastating than for her to come

here believing Clare to be cherishing the memory of her son only to learn that she had pledged herself to someone else. There was, of course, the possibility of keeping her in blissful ignorance, but as Clare was totally inexperienced in the art of subterfuge she dismissed the idea immediately.

Luke was regarding her intently, waiting for her comment, but a suitable one evaded her and it was with a deep inward sigh of relief that she saw her brother come back and sit down at the table.

'Your drink's on its way,' he told Luke, who thanked him and leant back in his chair, and from then on they all chatted together, mainly about Luke's new project until, at half-past ten, he rose and left them.

Clare stood at the barrier, her feelings mixed as she waited for the arrival through Customs of Mrs Weedall, for although it was less than three months since she had seen her, it seemed more like three years. So much had happened; she had not only adapted to a totally new environment, but had almost thrown off her unhappiness . . . had come near to the threshold of a new and exciting life.

'Clare!' The exclamation brought her mind back to the present and she forced a smile to her lips as she held out her hands to the woman who seemed, on looking back now, to have dominated her life from the moment Clare had met her son. 'Oh, but it's good to see you, child! I've been so impatient to get here! What a long, boring flight it is from London to Miami!'

'It does take a long time,' agreed Clare, taking Mrs Weedall's thin cold hands in hers and leaning forward to kiss her cheek. 'But you're here now, and it's nice to see you.' Stooping, she picked up the two suitcases from the trolley, surprised that they were far larger and heavier than she would have expected. How long, she wondered, was Mrs Weedall intending to stay? 'I have Phil's car just outside,' she said smiling, and glanced round to find a porter.

'Isn't it beautiful here?' commented Mrs Weedall as the porter dealt with her luggage. 'I believe I'm going to like it very much. We've had such dreadful weather at home, and it's been so cold that I've had an enormous expense with the heating. And Simon's never been round to see to the jobs that want doing. I was glad when the idea came to me to pay you a visit, Clare, dear—and thank you, child, for wanting me. You're the only person in the world who thinks anything about me, for I'm sure neither Simon nor his flighty young wife care whether I'm dead or alive.' The last word ended on a small sob and her footsteps flagged, making it necessary for Clare to slow down. But the porter went on ahead.

'This car?' he thumbed towards it and Clare nodded. He put the cases on the back seat and after handing him his tip Clare saw her visitor into the car and, going round to the other side, slipped into the driver's seat.

'It isn't far,' she said soothingly as Mrs Weedall leant back against the upholstery as if she were exhausted. 'I expect you're wanting a nice cool drink and a freshen up?'

'I am, dear. Phil didn't mind providing me with a room?'

'Of course not. You're going to have one of the very best in the hotel, one facing the sea with a balcony where you can sit out and relax. You can even have your meals sent up there if you like,' she added, but was instantly told that Mrs. Weedall had no wish to be alone except at night.

'I've been going out of my mind,' she confessed, a great sigh that was almost a sob coming from deep in her throat. 'The weeks going by and me never speaking to a soul, and my only diversion the weekly visit to my darling Frank's grave. Can you imagine, Clare, just how empty my life has been?'

'Yes, indeed I can.' Clare swallowed the hard little lump in her throat and fell silent, concentrating on her driving. Not that driving in Flamingo Cay was in any way difficult; on the contrary, since what little traffic there was moved at a slow leisurely pace with everyone practising patience and, more important, courtesy. No one could remember when the last road accident had occurred on the island.

'The scenery's beautiful.' Mrs Weedall was looking out all the time, absorbing everything as they rolled along the narrow, tree-shaded road. 'Is this the town you spoke of in your letters, dear?' she asked as they passed through the one main street of Cottonstown. 'It's very small to be the capital.'

'Yes,' laughed Clare, 'it is. You see, the island's small, as I told you in my letter. But it's so attractive, and as for the town—well, it grows on you very quickly.'

'You can't get all you want here, surely?'

Clare shook her head. 'No. We get important commodities from Miami. It's quite a simple matter to go over there—twenty minutes by air—and order what you want. It then comes over within a couple of weeks or so.' She was thinking of the tremendous amount of supplies which she would be requiring in the near future when her work for Luke began.

'Is someone looking after Frank's grave while you're away?' asked Clare after a while. She felt sure that some provision would have been made for the grave to be attended to.

'Yes, Simon did agree to do that. He or Susan will go every Saturday and change the flowers. I've left the money so they've no excuse for not carrying out my wishes.'

Every Saturday. . . . Clare's nerves tingled. She would have liked to ask how long her guest was staying but refrained, deciding it was not the thing to do.

On arrival at the Rusty Pelican Clare had one of the porters take Mrs Weedall's luggage up to her room on the first floor. Like the one occupied by Stella Wesley, it had recently been newly decorated and furnished, and Mrs Weedall was suitably impressed with it.

'It's a lovely bed-sitter,' she said looking all around. 'I haven't stayed in an hotel for over twenty-five years. Do they always have couches and desks and nice easy chairs nowadays?'

'Not always, but very often they do.' Clare walked over to a door and opened it, bringing an exclamation to Mrs Weedall's pale lips as she showed her the bathroom.

'I like it all very much. It's most comfortable.'

She stood for a moment, as if wanting to take it all in; Clare watched her, noticing the thinness of the features, the sagging jaw, the hollows beneath the cheekbones, the drooping mouth, pale and parched at the sides. Her hair was almost white and so sparse that the scalp showed pinkly through it. She had no need to look so much older than her age, decided Clare, wishing that Susan, her daughter-in-law, would take some interest in her, encouraging her to make herself more attractive.

'Do you want to come down and have afternoon tea with Phil and me?' she inquired at last. 'You'll want to freshen up first, though?'

'Yes, dear, I do feel like having a wash and combing my hair. And I would certainly be happy to have tea with you and Phil. Perhaps you'll wait for me?' she added uncertainly. 'I wouldn't know where to go otherwise.'

'Of course I'll wait,' replied Clare reassuringly. 'Shall I begin your unpacking while you're in the bathroom?'

'That's kind, dear. Yes, I'd like you to unpack my cases.'

Clare began with the smaller of the two, heaving it onto the bed and opening it up, thinking what a lot of clothes Mrs Weedall had brought and hoping that she had heeded her advice about bringing only summer clothes and, perhaps a cardigan and an evening wrap.

She hung the dresses in the wardrobe and put the underwear in the drawers. Then she saw, close to the bottom of the case, and wrapped carefully in a brand new evening shawl, a gilt-framed double photo frame. . . . It was closed but Clare knew what she would find on opening it. Yes, Frank's photograph and one of his father. Clare bit her lip, tears filling her eyes. To lose both husband and son. . . . Pity welled up as she reflected on what Mrs Weedall had said a short while ago. She, Clare was the only person in the world who thought anything about her. It was true, since her son scarcely ever went to see her, and in fact it had surprised Clare to learn that he had agreed to tend Frank's grave while his mother was away. 'I shall make this visit a happy and memorable time for her to remember.' was Clare's fervent vow as, reverently, she placed the frame on the bedside table and continued unpacking. Mrs Weedall reappeared from the bathroom and stood for a moment, looking at the empty suitcase which Clare was about to take from the bed.

'Ah . . . you've put darling Frank's photo there, by the bed. What do you think of that one, Clare? It was taken just before he knew you so I guess you haven't seen it before?'

'No . . . I haven't seen that one before.'

'It's a good one of him don't you think?'

Clare nodded and said yes, it was a very good one. She felt strangely numbed, as if part of her brain were paralysed and unable to function. She had several photographs of Frank, but at her mother's request had left them at home. And now she felt she should have experienced some emotional reaction in finding the photograph and handling it, but there was none.

'Is anything the matter, dear?' inquired Mrs Weedall anxiously. 'You seem troubled. Is it because of Frank's photograph? But you must have some of your own, and I'm sure you have one by your bed, so that you can look at it every night before you go to sleep?'

Clare's throat went dry. She looked at Frank's mother through a mist of tears, wanting to tell her the truth, and yet not for anything in the world would she upset her. And so she lied, deciding that a lie was permissible under the present circumstances. 'Yes,' she answered, avoiding her eyes, 'I do have Frank's photograph by my bed.'

'I knew it. And I'm so glad, Clare, that you're remembering. As I've always said, if it had been you who had died then Frank would have cherished your dear memory for ever.'

Clare turned away. She had gone pale and the palms of her hands were damp. She saw herself as a traitor, a girl who even now was deceiving a woman who trusted her implicitly.

'Shall we go for that tea, Clare?' Mrs Weedall's quiet voice cut her thoughts and she turned, nodding her head absently.

'Yes—yes, of course. You must be more than ready for it.'

'It'll be nice to see Phil again. I expect he's bronzed and healthy—just as Frank was after that holiday you both took in Spain, remember?'

'Yes—of course.' Clare led the way to the lift and pressed the bell. 'It was six years ago.'

'That other couple went with you—some friends of yours—didn't they?'

'That's right.'

'I expect they're married now.'

'Yes, they are.' The light above her head flickered and then came on. 'The lift'll be here directly.'

'Have they any children?'

'Two.'

'One of each?'

'No, two boys.'

'Like I did. If you and Frank had married I feel you'd have had at least four. I'd have liked that. I don't think Simon and Sue are intending to have any at all. It's a selfish attitude if you ask me.'

'Some people aren't cut out to be parents.'

'But you and Frank were. I'll never forget you

with that little girl who came to visit me one time—'

'The lift's here,' interrupted Clare, her nerve-ends ragged. They stepped into it and a few minutes later they were on the terrace, where a wrought-iron table and chairs were always reserved at this time for Phil and Clare.

'Sit down,' invited Clare, bringing out a chair. 'I'll go and see where Phil is.'

'What a charming setting this hotel has! Don't rush, Clare, dear, I'm very happy just to sit here for a few minutes and watch what's going on. Just look at all those young people down there on the beach. How dear Frank would have loved to have a holiday in a place like this!'

Clare moved away, her face still white, and much to her dismay she ran into Luke the moment she was out of Mrs Weedall's sight. 'What are you doing here at this time?' she wanted to know, so taken aback that she did not realise how abrupt her words would sound.

He looked down at her, his face suddenly taut. 'Your visitor has arrived,' he stated, ignoring her question. 'And you're not very happy about it. Why?'

She blinked, fluttering a trembling hand through her hair to take it from her eyes. 'What do you mean—why?'

'Exactly what I say. Why aren't you happy?'

'You reach the oddest conclusions,' she retorted pettishly.

'Correct all the same. Where is she?'

'On the terrace. I'm looking for Phil. We're going to have tea.'

'Mind if I join you?'

She shook her head in a sort of urgent gesture. 'Not today, Luke—er—she wouldn't want a stranger just now. She's tired and—well—' She broke off, floundering because of the way he was looking at her and because she had no real excuse to offer for not wanting him to take tea with them.

His mouth was tight, his eyes glinting with anger. 'If she's got you like this already,' he rasped, 'then what are you going to be like by the end of her stay—?' He broke off then asked, 'How long will she be here?'

'I don't know,' Clare answered, dismayed by the knowledge that she was very close to tears. 'She's brought a lot of clothes.'

'She has? And what about this grave she attends every week? She'll not want to leave that for very long.'

'Her other son's looking after it. I didn't tell you about Simon, did I?' She scarcely knew what she was saying; she did know that all she wanted was to get away before she burst into tears.

'No, you didn't tell me about Simon and as I'm not in the least interested you needen't feel guilty about the omission.'

'There's no need for sarcasm!' she flashed. 'Simon's her other son. He's married and either he or his wife will look after the grave.'

'Most interesting. And why, might I ask, are you telling me all this?' He towered over her, forbidding and imperious.

'You asked me who was looking after the grave.' She twisted her head, to see if they were attracting any attention. But what few guests were in the hotel were either taking tea or on the beach. 'I'll have to go,' she pleaded urgently. 'Will you find Phil for me and tell him where we are?'

For answer he took her arm and led her gently into the lounge. She went meekly, unable to fight him—unable, in fact, to explain what was wrong with her.

'Sit down,' he ordered, 'and I'll get you a drink.'

She obeyed, leaning back to find a resting place for her head. 'Mrs Weedall will wonder where I am,' she began when Luke, not bothering to call a waiter, brought her a drink from the bar.

'She'll not run away,' he assured her, and she was certain he added under his breath, 'More's the pity.'

'I can't leave her many minutes, Luke,' she began. 'If Phil were with her it would be all right.'

'What's she been saying to you?' he demanded, bypassing her words. 'You looked shattered just now.'

'It was nothing,' quivered Clare, lifting her glass in obedience to a gesture he made. 'She—

she naturally wanted to talk about Frank and
it—it upset me.'

'You're almost in tears,' he observed wrathfully.

'It's just reaction.'

'To what?'

'Oh, please—don't keep on questioning me!'
she cried. 'I want to go back to her.'

'When you've had your drink and you're more
settled.' He paused, then said decisively, 'I'm
having a word with Phil.'

'Oh, no, please don't interfere, Luke! Promise!'

'I'm promising nothing—except,' he added,
'that I shall join you for tea. I want to take a look
at this visitor of yours.'

Chapter Eight

Clare was both troubled and angry as she made
her way back to where she had left her visitor on
the terrace. Luke's attitude, imperious and determined, had created a resentment within her
that almost matched that which she had har-

boured against him right at the beginning
when, probably unknown to himself, his personality had affected her so strongly that it was
often his image that intruded when all she
desired was to see that of her dead fiancé. Luke
had decided he had the right to interfere if he
thought that she was being upset by Mrs Weedall. Clare knew very well on what basis he
claimed this right: it was his feelings for her.
But as he had not declared openly that he loved
her—and would never do so until she gave him
some concrete evidence of her own love—he had
no command over her at all. It was understandable that he should be angry on seeing her upset, but to put it bluntly he ought to mind his
own business; her welfare was not in any way
his concern at the present time. It was all very
illogical, Clare admitted, because one part of
her mind *wanted* it to be his concern, wishing
he *did* have the right to interfere.

But for the present her own sentiments were
unimportant. What was important was that Mrs
Weedall should not be hurt by anything Luke or
anyone else should say. She had come here in all
good faith, expecting to be treated as an invited
guest should be treated, and Clare was determined to do all in her power to ensure that she
enjoyed every minute of her stay.

'Phil will be here in a few minutes', she smiled
as she sat down, hesitating a moment before
adding, 'Another man's joining us for tea. I hope
you don't mind?'

'No. . . . Well, I'm a shy sort of person, as you

know, Clare, and I suppose it's from being alone so much. However, I must get used to people if I'm to be staying here, mustn't I?'

'It'll be good for you to mix, Mrs Weedall. We all need company at times.'

'Yes—I'm sure you're right, dear. Er—who is this man? Is he one of the hotel guests?'

'No, he's a friend of Phil's and he lives here, on Flamingo Cay, in a beautiful house called Silver Springs. His name's Luke Mortimer.'

'He must be rich.'

'He is. He's just bought an island.' The information escaped mechanically and Clare regretted having offered it the moment it was voiced.

'An island?' The older woman's pale eyes widened to their fullest extent. 'One like this?'

'Not as large as this.'

'Is he going to live there?'

'No, he intends developing it—partly. He's building three hotels on it. There's nothing much on it at all at present.'

'Won't the building spoil it?'

'No, Mrs Weedall, it will not be spoiled.' She glanced around, looking for Phil and Luke but there was no sign of them. 'Are you very thirsty, Mrs Weedall? Shall I have a pot of tea brought to us now and we can have it while we're waiting?'

'No, thank you, Clare. I must admit I'm thirsty but if you say Phil will be here soon then I can wait. You were talking about this gentleman who's joining us,' she went on, her pale eyes curious. 'Is he a young man?'

'About thirty-five, I think.'

'Young to be so wealthy,' mused Mrs Weedall. 'Is he married?'

Clare shook her head, and for a fleeting moment there flashed before her eyes the beautiful face of Stella Wesley. Luke would have been married if she had not jilted him. . . . 'No, he's not married.'

'It sounds as if he devotes himself entirely to business?'

'Yes, mainly he does. He buys land and develops it. He's bought several large plots of land here on Flamingo Cay.'

'For building on?'

Clare nodded. 'Yes, of course.'

Mrs Weedall fell silent for a moment, her attention having been arrested by a graceful white-sailed yacht that was coming into the marina. 'If Frank could only have seen all this. . . .' She spoke to herself, her voice a dull monotone. She appeared to have forgotten Clare's presence altogether as she went on, 'And if he could ever have afforded to buy an island he'd have kept it exactly as it was.' She looked up, into Clare's face. 'He loved nature and natural things—but why am I telling you this when you already know? Do you remember the rambles you used to take on Sundays—across the moors—and come back exhausted, and I'd have a lovely meal ready and we'd all sit over it and you'd both tell us what you'd seen and done? Those were the happiest days of my life, Clare, when we were all together—Frank and his

father and you and me. And I know I'm right
when I say they were the happiest days of your
life.' She lapsed into silence, inviting a response
but Clare said nothing. She was feeling stifled,
and a nerve-twisting tension was building up
inside her. 'You have memories, though, dear
Clare,' continued Mrs Weedall in her thin, ex-
pressionless voice. 'Have you ever stopped to
think what your life would be if you didn't have
such beautiful memories?'

Clare looked at her, wondering what she
would say if she were to tell her that the
memories had been fading until she came,
bringing them all back with poignant intensity.
'They certainly are beautiful memories,' she
forced herself to say.

'And they'll last forever,' she heard Mrs Weedall assert triumphantly. 'You're the loyal and
faithful kind, Clare, and I know just what I
missed when I didn't get you for a daughter. My
darling Frank would have been so blessed and so
would I.' Tears filled the pale colourless eyes and
as Clare watched, fascinated without knowing
why, two big tears rolled unchecked down her
face. Pity welled up, flooding Clare's whole
being and on impulse she reached across the
table to cover Mrs Weedall's hand with her own.
And it was at that moment that the two men
appeared, to stand in silence for a space, staring
down at the two hands touching.

Clare glanced up, withdrawing her hand
swiftly. Luke's face was marble hard, set and

stern but otherwise unreadable, while Phil, after greeting Mrs Weedall with his customary politeness, introduced Luke to her and then, offering her a charming smile, asked her about the flight, and about her health. But beneath the gracious exterior Clare sensed anger and resentment. Luke had done his work well, obviously having convinced Phil that, even at this early stage, Mrs Weedall had succeeded in making Clare unhappy.

The two men sat down; the waiter appeared with the sandwiches and cakes, and while Clare poured the tea Luke spoke to Mrs Weedall, his manner aloof but polite, and Clare was thankful for small mercies. Her glance during the meal spoke volumes as she silently begged Luke not to say anything to hurt her guest. Mrs Weedall seemed shy and diffident with him, answering his questions in monosyllables and invariably avoiding the direct glances he often sent in her direction.

'I can't say I care very much for Phil's friend,' she was confiding to Clare an hour later when they were walking slowly along the beach, the breeze from the sea delightfully cool on their faces. 'He's rather frightening, isn't he?'

'Frightening, Mrs Weedall?' Even as she spoke Clare was recalling with a wry grimace her own experiences of just how frightening he could be when angered.

'He's stern and—formidable, and a snob, I think.'

'He's often rather arrogant,' Clare agreed.

'He's that kind of man. But he has other traits that are very attractive.'

'He has?' Mrs Weedall almost stopped to look searchingly into her companion's face. 'Do you know him well?' she asked.

'Er—quite well, yes. He comes to the Rusty Pelican often for dinner or for a drink in the evening. Most of the residents do; they use the hotel as a sort of club. In England it would be their local.'

'I see. And so of course you're very friendly with him?'

Clare's nerves tingled, on the alert. Diplomacy was required, and would be required throughout Mrs Weedall's stay on the island. And if diplomacy meant a white lie now and then, so be it. 'Not *very* friendly, Mrs Weedall. He's Phil's friend; they've known one another for over a year, while I've known Luke for just over two months.'

'It's a wonder he doesn't have a girl-friend. Handsome men like him usually do have one— even if they've no intention of marrying them.'

'He's had girl-friends I believe.'

'But he doesn't have one now?'

'No,' she answered, feeling that this was fairly close to the truth because she and Luke were not actually keeping company.

They walked on in silence for a time, and as Clare cast her companion a sideways glance she noticed with satisfaction that her face had taken on a complacent expression as if she were thoroughly enjoying the stroll along a beach of powder-soft sand. 'Do you know, Clare,' she began as they turned eventually to retrace their steps, 'this is the first time I've ever seen coconut palms growing.'

'I hadn't seen them until I came here.'

'There's something fascinating about it, isn't there?'

'Yes—and about all the other exotic plants and trees you see here. The lovely vine that you saw on the terrace is bougainvillaea, and the bushes close by are hibiscus.'

'I must take some snapshots to show Simon and Sue.' A small pause and then, 'If only Frank were here. Wouldn't he just love all this? And he was such an excellent swimmer as you know. He'd have enjoyed the diving. . . . Those men over there are diving down into the coral gardens, aren't they?'

'Yes—well, they've just come up. We can take a trip on a glass-bottomed boat if you like, and see the coral gardens from a comfortable seat on board.'

'That would be nice.' Her smile was a weak attempt. 'My Frank could swim from the age of three. His dad took him to the baths every week-end, and everyone became interested in Frank because he was so young to be swimming.' She continued to reminisce, her voice quiet, monotonous, but her tone at times took on a whining quality which set Clare's teeth on edge. 'Are you going to your room to rest?' she asked as soon as they arrived back at the hotel.

'Yes, I think so. What should I wear for dinner?' she wanted to know, her voice edged with a tinge of anxiety. 'Simon said it's all informal nowadays and you don't need to dress up unless it's specially requested for some reason.'

'You don't need to dress up,' Clare agreed, but went on to say that she usually wore a long dress because she liked to be different in the evenings. 'A long skirt and frilly blouse would be all right,' she suggested. 'You used to wear frilly blouses, I remember.'

'Yes, because both Frank and his father liked me in them. Frank had such excellent taste in women's clothes, didn't he?'

'Yes,' replied Clare, quite unable to remember whether he had or not.

'He told me he would have liked to design your wedding dress but you'd ordered it before he had time to suggest it.'

'Oh—I didn't know.' It was all coming back with aching poignancy—the dress, delectable with its flowing skirt and tight-fitting bodice, the bridesmaids' gowns, the rehearsal in the church, the presents and invitations, the booking of the hall for the reception, the arrangements for the honeymoon. . . . And all leading up to—what . . . ? Oh, God—stop! Unconsciously Clare put her hands to her eyes as if by the frenzied action she could shut out for ever the terrible anguish of the final scene, enacted in a churchyard. . . .

'Well,' said Mrs Weedall, obviously unaware of Clare's distress, 'he wouldn't tell you because he didn't want to upset you. But it was a disappointment to him, and it's a pity, now, looking back,

that he didn't speak up in time. . . .' She stopped
reflectively and Clare seized the opportunity of
bringing her attention to the time and pointing
out that if she wanted to rest she ought to be
going to her room at once.

'Phil and I usually have dinner at about
half-past eight,' she added finally. She was
endeavouring to maintain a veneer of calm as
she spoke but her nerves were stretched almost
to the breaking point and she felt that if she
could scream it would bring untold relief.

'I'll leave you then, dear. And thank you so
much for the lovely walk on the beach. It was
kind of Phil to give you time off to be with me.
It's wonderful not to be lonely for a change. I do
sincerely thank you, Clare, for inviting me here
to this lovely island.' She seemed to falter on her
last words and, glancing at her, Clare saw the
moisture in her eyes. A terrible lump rose in
Clare's throat; her voice was jerky and edged
with tears as she said, 'Don't thank me, Mrs
Weedall, it's a—a pleasure having you.' She
managed to accompany her to the lift and then
she turned away abruptly, because the deluge of
pity enveloping her was finding an outlet in
tears. They rolled unchecked down her cheeks
as she hastily made her way towards a corridor
and a flight of stairs which would take her to the
floor where her bedroom was situated. But first
she had to pass the door of her brother's office.
She was half-way along the corridor and almost
running, when to her chagrin and dismay she

saw Luke emerge from the office and close the door behind him. He gave a start on seeing her in such a hurry, and noting her tears he exclaimed, 'Clare—what's wrong—?' Then he stopped, his eyes narrowing to mere slits. 'Why are you crying?' he demanded harshly. 'That woman! What's been happening? You've been with her since teatime?'

'Yes, but—it's nothing to do with you—'

'By God, it is!' His action was as swift as his words, and Clare had no time to escape before he had gripped her by the arms, his fingers digging painfully into her flesh. 'She's been upsetting you,' he rasped, 'and it's not going to happen again—'

'Leave me alone!' she cried, every nerve twisted and knotted inside her. 'It's none of your business!' Managing to break free of his punishing hold, she sped away in the direction of the stairs, conscious of his voice calling in anger and concern, but relieved that he made no attempt to come after her.

By dinner time she was calm and composed, having surprised herself by her miraculous recovery from what at the time had been near hysteria. She had taken a bath and washed her hair, and while sitting under the dryer she had reached a state of composure. Her normal rational thinking returned and she could face her present situation objectively. It was plain that Mrs Weedall would continue to talk about her son, and it was plain too that she genuinely believed Clare to be entirely in sympathy with her, content to be recalling memories. And in all fairness Clare had to admit that before she came here, she *had* been content to recall memories. She would never have dreamed of missing her Saturday visit to the grave, when she and Frank's mother would share their labour of love while talking sadly about Frank and the tragedy of his early death. Now by some miracle Clare had not only managed to put the past from her but had even contemplated a new life with another man as her husband. Mrs Weedall had brought the memories with her across three thousand miles of ocean with the intention of sharing them with Clare. So it would seem that in order to remain calm Clare must resign herself to listening to Mrs Weedall and contributing to the conversation, even though the part she played was specious. When Clare had eventually come out from under the dryer the newly-made resolve was fixed right in the forefront of her mind.

The dress she wore was coral-coloured Thai silk, which she had bought during a Thai Week at one of London's leading stores. Loose-fitting with enormous folds falling from the sleeves to the waist and down the full length of the skirt, it was perhaps too dressy for tonight, but she was determined to wear it because it always did something for her ego. She knew it was sheer perfection, that when she walked the length of the restaurant all eyes would be turned towards her. It always happened that way and on the first occasion Clare had been so embarrassed that it was a long time before she ventured to wear the dress again. However, she did wear it, and had worn it several times since, always with the same result. Tonight, she needed just this admiration to complete the cure, to restore fully her composure and ease of mind.

To her surprise a larger table had replaced the table for four which was always in its place by the window with the view over the marina. Phil was already there talking to Luke who, attired in a cream-coloured lightweight suit with a white shirt and dark tie, made his usual arresting figure, pride and arrogance in his entire bearing. She looked up at him, recalling vividly the last time they had met, so very briefly, in the corridor. His present manner was different from what she expected for somehow she had prepared herself for hostility, if only in its mildest form. Instead—apart from the hint of mockery in his eyes—it savoured strongly of indifference. His greeting was casual; his attention as he took out the chair and stood away from her was no less impersonal than if he had been rendering the service to a near stranger. Her heart sank and her lip quivered; she averted her head so that he should not see what his cool detachment was doing to her.

But if she had been dejected before her spirits were swept into the depths of despair when, on asking why the table had been changed, she was told by Luke that Stella Wesley was dining with them, and would be here shortly.

'Mrs Wesley!' she exclaimed before she had time to prevent the words becoming an exclamation.

'Yes,' replied Luke, 'Mrs Wesley—but you can call her Stella, she prefers it. After all,' he added—and Clare was sure there was an edge of malice to his tone—'we're all friends together, aren't we?'

'Are we?' She flashed a glance in her brother's direction as she spoke. Almost imperceptibly he shrugged, as if telling her that although he was far from pleased at the idea of having Stella at their table, he was not intending to offend either Luke or one of the hotel guests. And with his swift change of expression he was telling her to adopt the same attitude but she ignored it on recollecting Stella's downright rudeness on her arrival at the hotel. 'As far as I am concerned, Luke,' she said coolly, turning to him, 'Mrs Wesley is no different from any other guest in the hotel.'

'Perhaps, Clare, but she happens to be interested in buying one of my properties in Miami, and that's why I invited her to dine with us. I hope you'll be nice to her.'

She lifted her eyes, to meet his in a cold, direct glance. Phil, alert to the tension building between them, opened his mouth to intervene but was prevented from speaking by one of the hotel guests coming up to him to make some sort of inquiry. It gave Clare the chance of saying, 'I shall be civil to her, Luke, but I don't consider myself obliged to fawn over her just because she's a potential customer of yours!'

'I haven't asked you to fawn. . . .' His voice rolled into silence, his eyes widening for one fleeting moment before his expression became an unfathomable mask. But Clare knew what that widening of his eyes had meant. . . .

She had spoken hotly, stabbed with jealousy of his old flame, having her doubts about her interest in his property and being more inclined to suspect her of using that excuse to win her ex-fiancé's interest in herself. But already Clare was regretting her impulsive outburst, for in that brief moment when Luke's eyes had widened, she realised with dismay that he had gleaned an insight into her feelings. He knew that she was jealous of Stella.

Bitterly regretting her unthinking outburst, she sought vainly for words that would effectively disabuse him, convince him he was wrong in believing her to be jealous of his old flame. But resignedly she admitted that no matter what she added at this stage it would merely strengthen his conviction rather than weaken it.

In any case, Mrs Weedall had arrived and, in his usual polite way, Phil was greeting her with a smile. 'Ah, Mrs Weedall. Do sit down—here.' He was pulling out a chair for her and she accepted it, thanking him diffidently. Luke's eyes were contemptuous; they passed from her face to Clare's and then he appeared to lose

interest in both of them as his gaze settled on
one particularly beautiful yacht in the marina,
its sails fluttering in the breeze. Dozens of other
yachts were there, the lights from their masts
creating dancing silver stars on the surface of
the water.

Mrs Weedall was speaking, saying she had
managed to have a nap.

'I'm glad.' Clare sent her a smile, her glance
taking in the white blouse with its familiar frill
running from neck to hem. 'It'll have done you
good after that flight, and then the walk on the
beach. You've had a very busy time since yesterday.'

'Yes, indeed.' Clare looked furtively in Luke's
direction but his attention was elsewhere—on
Stella, whose svelte figure swayed in tempting,
sexy movements as she made her majestic way
to the table.

She sat down next to Luke, and all through the
meal Clare, seated opposite, was forced to en-
dure the bewitching activities of the girl's exper-
tise in making herself attractive to a man. She
fluttered her long dark lashes, had a way of
twisting her head so that the glory of her hair
was brought to his notice. She whispered to him
and he nodded interestedly; she even used her
elegant, perfectly-manicured hands, spreading
them as an accompaniment to some remark,
holding the two middle fingers together in the
manner of a ballet-dancer.

Now and then Luke would slide Clare a

glance, his face unmoving, without expression. She decided to adopt a couldn't-care-less attitude, and give most of her attention to her visitor.

Chapter Nine

Tears touched Clare's lashes as she watched the couple dancing, their bodies close, Luke's head bent so that his lips seemed to be caressing Stella's temple. Luke had come to the Rusty Pelican for dinner but instead of joining Phil and Clare and their guest he had occupied another table, having brought as his companion the glamorous girl to whom he was once engaged. And it did seem to Clare that they had already resumed some aspects of their old relationship, for Clare's covert glances had several times caught Luke laughing; and the way his companion looked at him, a winning smile on her lips, seemed to indicate that the two were certainly happy to be in each other's company.

Grudgingly Clare had to admit that they made a striking couple, both being tall and stately, with smooth majestic movements reminiscent of royalty.

Clare's misery was not helped by Mrs Weedall's casual remark to Phil, 'Your friend seems rather struck with Mrs Wesley, doesn't he?'

'I sincerely hope he isn't,' from Phil tautly. 'I'd hate the idea of her coming to live—' He stopped abruptly, conscious of the fact that he had broken his rule of never uttering a disparaging word about one guest in front of another. Not that Mrs Weedall was an ordinary guest; nevertheless, as he was to say to Clare afterwards, it was not right to have said anything at all about the woman, however objectionable she might have been.

'She's very beautiful.' Mrs Weedall seemed fascinated by the couple on whom all eyes were turned. 'She's a widow, you were saying, Clare?'

'Yes, that's right.' Clare was also fascinated. Luke's eyes met hers fleetingly; his expression changed and what she saw was a cold handsome face with a hard unyielding mouth. Clare lowered her eyes, but not before his expression had changed again and he was smiling charmingly down into his partner's face.

'I hate her,' breathed Clare silently, the fierce barbs of jealousy piercing her heart. 'She's poison! Surely Luke knows that she's hard and horrid and everything that he dislikes!' But she was recalling Luke's assertion that all men admire beauty, and whatever Stella Wesley lacked it was certainly not beauty—no, she possessed that in abundance.

The music stopped and the couple sat down, Luke's eyes sliding momentarily to Clare's table.

'I'm rather surprised that Luke wanted to dine alone with that woman,' Phil was saying later when he and Clare were on their own, having a drink in the Clipper Inn, Mrs Weedall having decided to go to bed earlier than usual. She had been on the island for over a week and appeared to be enjoying herself despite the fact that scarcely an hour passed without her mentioning her dead son. Clare, having made her resolve to be patient, was gradually gaining the ability to control her nerves, and to smile and act as if she were still cherishing her love for Frank.

'She and he were once engaged.' Clare had not previously mentioned the fact to her brother, although she could find no reason for her reticence.

'Engaged?' Phil's brows lifted incredulously. 'He told you?'

Clare nodded her head. 'Yes, he told me. It was six years ago.'

'What happened?' The couple under discussion had come into the bar and were standing there, deciding where to sit, and Phil's eyes were drawn to them. Luke—who had previously spent a few moments at Phil's table, chatting with him—lifted a hand and smiled, but he never even glanced at Clare, who was frowning heavily. Luke scarcely ever came into the Clipper Inn, preferring the lounge of the hotel. Why, then, should he have come in here tonight? Surely he would know that she would be upset at seeing him give so much attention to his old flame. It was almost as if he were deliberately trying to hurt Clare, by flaunting his glamorous companion before her eyes all the time. But on considering this, Clare thrust it away, refusing to believe that Luke would do a thing like that to her. It was probably at Stella's suggestion that they had come in here for their after dinner drinks.

'She married someone else. He died six months ago.'

'She threw Luke over?' Phil's manner was disbelieving as his eyes strayed yet again to the couple who were now occupying a table which was in full view of where he and Clare were sitting. 'I can't believe that he'd be as friendly as this if she'd served him that sort of trick.'

'I must admit that it puzzles me too,' returned Clare, hoping that the little sob in her throat had escaped her brother's notice. She was so unhappy she could have burst into tears. She felt sure she had lost Luke, and through her own fault. He had become tired of her inconsistent behaviour and had probably decided that she was of an unreliable type—no use to him at all. These and many other dismal thoughts were running through her mind when one of them was voiced by Phil.

'It would be pretty grim if he married her and she came to live on Flamingo Cay.'

A painful tightness settled in Clare's throat. 'The possibility's already occurred to me,' she said.

'Well, if that happened the friendship between Luke and me would be finished. I could never accept that woman and I'm sure you couldn't either.' Phil was troubled as he continued to watch the couple, laughing and chatting and certainly getting along exceedingly well together. Clare, conscious of Luke's eyes on her now and then, avoided them if she could. But Stella caught Clare's eyes a couple of times and there was no mistaking her look of sneering triumph. She was getting her own back for that occasion when Luke had bidden her a formal goodnight, saying that he and Clare had something private to talk about. Stella had been furious, Clare remembered, but now it was her turn to have all of Luke's attention.

Suddenly Clare decided that if there was the slightest possibility of a marriage between Luke and Stella, then she would return to England with Mrs Weedall when she went back at the end of her holiday. The decision would make her parents unhappy, but there was nothing else she could do but return to England, simply because never in a million years would she get used to the idea of Stella being mistress of Silver Springs, wife to its owner. But how could she tell for sure that Luke was intending to take up where he and his old flame had left off?

Clare wanted to find out before Mrs Weedall left. . . . She must not risk coming to the wrong conclusion, and it suddenly struck her that there was only one sure way, and although it would mean embarrassment she decided to act on the idea. She would ask Luke outright if there was any possibility of him and Mrs Wesley becoming engaged again.

Meanwhile, though, something else had been troubling Clare and she said, changing the subject, 'Phil, is it possible that I could have another week off? I hate to ask but Mrs Weedall will be on her own if I can't—'

'Don't look so troubled,' broke in her brother gently. 'By all means take the week off. Mary won't mind at all; she likes the desk work as you know, and if you hadn't come along I'd probably have asked her to accept the post.'

'Thanks a lot, Phil,' returned Clare gratefully. 'Now I can keep her company. She'd be lonely on her own.' But the following morning Clare had something else to do and she asked Mrs Weedall if she could amuse herself for about an hour or so.

'Of course, Clare, dear,' she answered with a smile. 'I've brought my photograph albums with me so I'll sit and look through them. I have such lovely snapshots of you and dear Frank—what a handsome couple you were! I'll be sitting here, on the terrace, so you'll know where to find me.'

Clare went off immediately to visit Luke at Silver Springs. The grounds sparkled in the sunshine, the fountains creating rainbow cascades as they stole colours from the sun. Clare looked around, her heart feeling dead at the idea of a detestable girl like Stella Wesley becoming

mistress of all this. What was the matter with
Luke that he couldn't see through her? With
Clare herself he had always been more than
ordinarily perceptive. Clare could only conclude
that the girl's beauty was the draw.

She began to walk briskly on towards the
house, then realised that Stella was with Luke.
They were talking as they stood on the verandah
which fronted the main living-room of the villa.
Clare stopped, her heart jerking, then dropping
right down into her feet. There was really no
need for her question, she decided and, turning,
would have made her escape but Luke caught
sight of her flowered dress an instant before she
managed to dodge behind a wall.

'Clare!' His voice halted her and she turned,
her head held proudly, her eyes brittle and cold.
'What is it?'

He seemed concerned, she thought, watching
him come down the steps of the verandah,
leaving a frowning girl behind him. 'I didn't
know you had company,' returned Clare stiffly.
'It was nothing important—'

'It must have been, for you to have come here
to see me.' He was towering over her and as
always she knew the pull of his magnetism, the
attraction which, she now realised, she had
never known in her relationship with Frank,
much as she had loved him.

'It's nothing, really,' she was desperate to get
away before the bitter tears of jealousy and
regret filled her eyes, reflecting what was in her

heart. 'I'll probably see you tonight—or some-time,' she added casually.

But he was shaking his head in a determined gesture. 'Wait a minute and I'll be with you—'

'Your visitor—' Clare was so close to tears that her voice broke in the middle. 'You can't leave her, and in any case, it was nothing important. I'll talk to you again sometime!' And with that she hurried away, convinced that he would neither call her back nor follow her, not with Mrs Wesley being there, a witness to it all.

The tears fell readily once Clare was away from Silver Springs, running unhindered down her face. It was plain that Luke and his old flame were intending to take up where they had left off, and Clare knew exactly what she must do: return to England with Mrs Weedall.

A few hours after her brief visit to Silver Springs Clare was on the lawn with Mrs Weedall when suddenly the older woman said, 'Here's Phil's friend—'

'Luke!' Clare's heart gave an uncomfortable little jerk as she saw Luke striding towards where they were sitting in gaily-coloured loungers, Clare clad only in a bikini.

'He appears to be coming to speak to you,' said Mrs Weedall in her customary monotonous voice. 'I think I shall go in and take a rest, Clare, dear, for I'm never comfortable in that man's company.'

Luke reached them and for a space his eyes

roved Clare's scantily-clad figure, lingering on the enchanting curves before moving to her face, a touch of sardonic amusement curving his mouth as he noticed her heightened colour. Then he spared a glance for her companion, and obviously feeling it was incumbent on him to be sociable he tried to chat with her, but it was a fitful conversation interspersed with embarrassed pauses on Mrs Weedall's part, and at last she faltered apologetically, 'I think I shall take a rest—er—if you'll excuse me . . . ?'

Luke's eyes followed her for a moment, a frown darkening his eyes. 'I thought I'd come along to see why you paid me the honour of a visit to Silver Springs.' He was in white shorts, the sleeves of his shirt rolled up to the elbows. Deeply bronzed, and with the muscles of his strong limbs rippling, he seemed more attractive to Clare than ever. He was looking down at her, waiting for an answer.

'It was nothing important, Luke. As a matter of fact, I just thought I'd take a stroll and I found myself at your gate. . . .' Her voice trailed off to an embarrassed silence as she noted his expression, aware that he knew she was lying.

'Come off it, Clare,' he chided, casually taking possession of the lounger vacated by Mrs Weedall. 'You had something of importance to say to me and I demand to know what it was.'

'Demand?' she repeated, eyes sparkling.

'What was it?' he asked patiently.

'I'm no longer willing to say what I intended

saying,' she responded stubbornly and saw his mouth compress into a thin and angry line.

'You changed your mind because Stella was there—is that it?'

'Perhaps.'

'What do you mean, perhaps? Either it was or it wasn't.'

'Please don't be so persistent,' she begged. 'I really mean it when I say I've changed my mind.'

He made an exasperated little exclamation but realised by Clare's expression that to continue his questioning would avail him nothing. And so he changed the subject, his eyes sliding momentarily in the direction taken by Mrs Weedall. 'Your guest appears to be settled in.'

Clare breathed a sigh of relief and answered, 'Yes, she likes the island, and especially the hotel. We've given her one of the best rooms and she's very happy in it.'

'Happy?' with a sceptical lift of his straight dark brows. 'That woman's never been happy in the whole of her life.'

'Of course she has. She was never like this when Frank was alive.'

Luke drew a breath but said nothing, and after a space Clare thanked him for being so civil to Mrs Weedall. 'I feared at first that you were thinking of being unpleasant with her— especially when you said you'd sort something out.'

'I meant to sort something out,' he admitted

tersely. 'I intended to find a way of telling her outright that she was ruining your life, that it was time you forgot all about her dead son and began living again.'

Clare asked him curiously, 'What made you change your mind?'

'Pity,' he admitted. 'She's a most unhappy woman, and I've no patience with her; nevertheless, I'm still sorry for her—' He broke off, shrugging his shoulders. 'I suppose, basically, I'm soft.'

Clare had to smile at a statement like that! 'I'm glad you could feel pity for her, Luke. You'll understand a bit better now, won't you?'

'No,' he denied abruptly. 'I won't.'

It was Clare's turn to change the subject. 'How is everything going regarding the new project?' She would now be taking no part in it, she thought sadly. Perhaps Luke would ask Mrs Wesley to do it for him.

'Going well.'

'I'm glad.'

'You're very cold,' he said.

'I hadn't noticed.' She wanted him to go and yet, paradoxically, she desperately wanted him to stay with her, to speak gently to her, to look at her with that softened expression she had come to know so well.

'What's wrong?' His voice did seem a trifle softer, she thought, a little lump rising in her throat. 'Why don't you tell me, Clare?'

There was a curious ring to his voice, a sort of

expectancy, an eagerness, and if it had not been
for the fact that he had been giving Mrs Wesley
his attention lately Clare could almost have
believed that he was eagerly waiting for her to
say she loved him. And so she decided to ask the
question, although not in the forthright way she
had at first intended.

'It was merely an interest in your association
with Mrs Wesley,' she began when he interrupted her, eyes alert.

'You came over to Silver Springs to talk about
Stella?'

'No, of course not,' she lied, and hoped she
sounded convincing. 'I'm not telling you what I
came about.'

'All right,' exasperatedly and with a frown.
'Well, you were saying, you're interested in my
association with Stella. What is it you want to
know—whether we are thinking of going steady
again?'

Clare moistened her lips, contriving to appear
casual as she said, 'You were enjoying your-
selves last evening.' She coloured, wishing she
had not broached the subject after all. It was
Luke's manner that had made her do it, because
she desperately wanted to know if he was serious with the girl.

'Yes, we were,' he admitted reflectively. And
he seemed far away as he added, 'We talked
about old times. . . .' His eyes flickered to hers
but she had averted her head. Words were too
difficult to summon for a space but eventually
she was able to say, 'You could forgive her

for—for what she did? She married someone
else, you said?'

His face was impassive as he replied, 'Yes, I
have forgiven her.'

'You feel nothing—no grudge whatsoever?'

'None,' he replied in that same impassive tone
of voice. 'One cannot harbour a grudge forever.'
He paused, examining Clare's expression. 'What
makes you look at me like that?' he inquired.
'There's surprise on your face as well as puzzlement.'

'I suppose I've gained the impression that
you're not the forgiving type—' Her voice was
hollow because she was fighting tears. 'Obviously I was mistaken.'

Luke remained silent and she glanced up. He
said quietly, 'I intend to go to Windward Cay
tomorrow, Clare. Is it possible for you to come
with me?'

'You want *me*?' she said, her beautiful eyes
disbelieving.

'Who else?'

'But—you've just said that Mrs Wesley—that
you and she might—'

'Stella is pleasure, this is business, I never
mix the two. In any case, it happens to be you
who is helping me, not Stella.'

Clare felt a pulse tingle, and as she looked
steadily at him she was desperately trying to
read what was in his mind. 'You still want me to
help you, even though you are thinking of—of
marrying Mrs Wesley?'

'What difference does that make?' he inquired,

avoiding her gaze—a very strange circumstance, thought Clare, considering his habit of
always looking directly into her eyes when
speaking to her.

'Well . . . none, I suppose. But she might not
like it.'

For an instant his eyes hardened but when he
spoke his voice was pleasant enough. 'I never
allow anyone to interfere in my business, Clare.
I've engaged you to help me and my decision
stands.'

Her first instinct was to refuse Luke's offer,
telling him of her decision to return to England
and that, therefore, she would not be assisting
him after all, but she stopped herself. For the
idea of a full day with Luke on an uninhabited
island was so tempting that it overshadowed all
else. She found herself saying, a smile on her
lips, 'Yes, Luke, I'd love to see your island. It
means leaving Mrs Weedall on her own but
she'll not mind for one day. I expect we'll be
back in time for dinner?'

Luke's eyes had hardened slightly at her mention of Mrs Weedall, but he obviously decided not
to voice what was in his mind. 'Yes,' he said, 'we
shall be back for dinner.'

They went off very early the following morning and for Clare it could have been an idyllic
sail if only she and Luke were as they were
before the arrival on the island of his old flame.
But now the shadow of the girl lay within Clare's

vision and she was depressed. However, she was determined to be as happy as she could be under the circumstances and she chatted with Luke, making suggestions for the decor of the hotels and noting with pleasure that he was always favourably impressed.

'I knew instinctively that you would have excellent taste,' he said, a smile in his eyes that sent tingles of pleasure along her spine. 'I'm excited about the whole project, Clare, feeling sure we have something unique that was needed a long time ago.'

'It's a wonder no one thought about it,' mused Clare, a sigh of contentment escaping her as she gazed at the lovely island to which they were heading. A gem set in a sea of blue and gold and emerald green, its coconut and travellers' palms waving in the breeze, and the one low hill lush and green. Its lake gleamed in the sun, its long beaches were pink-tinted, and darker where the sea lapped their silent shores. Clare found herself forgetting Stella Wesley, and in fact everything except the thought of a day alone with Luke on this lovely island in the sun.

He had had a picnic hamper put up and after they had spent a couple of hours exploring, and Luke had shown her exactly where each of the hotels would be located, they found a place on the shore and ate delicious sandwiches washed down with fruity white wine. Strawberries and cream were served to her from sealed jars, and coffee from a flask.

'That was lovely.' Her smile shone up at him as he stood above her. Clare had taken off her shoes and Luke stared at her feet. Her dainty toenails were painted a delicate shade of honey-peach which matched her tan and Luke watched in some amusement as she moved her feet, relishing the delicious experience of talcum-soft sand between her toes.

'You're just a little girl, aren't you?' he said, and her heart caught because it seemed that his voice was tender, and because he was looking at her as she wanted him to, and because his hand had sought hers, covering it strongly, his thumb caressing. But as the day wore on her spirits began to sink, for Luke had not attempted even to kiss her, much less make love as she had fully expected him to. True, there was a great deal of work—making notes, putting forward suggestions for discussion, planning the gardens.

'Well, Clare, I think we've done a good day's work.' It was a quarter to five. He was looking at her, a half-smile on his lips. 'It's time we were getting back to Flamingo Cay.'

'Yes,' she agreed flatly, 'it is.'

Luke, his expression unfathomable, picked up the hamper and carried it to the jetty where the launch was moored. Somehow she had felt that in this visit to Windward Cay, she would be able to make Luke notice her again . . . to win him back from Stella Wesley, but she had done nothing. The opportunity had been lost . . . or perhaps it had never been there at all.

Chapter Ten

It was two days later that Mrs Weedall told Clare she was considering a prolonged stay on Flamingo Cay. 'I like it so much,' she added, with her usual thin smile. 'And I have you, which is so nice for me, Clare, dear. I've been so much alone and now everything's changed. Do you think that Phil can arrange for me to have a room for about three months?'

Three months! Consternation looked out from Clare's eyes. She recalled last evening, when Luke had again dined alone with Stella Wesley, giving her all his attention, obviously very happy to be with her. It still amazed Clare that he could not only have forgiven her but was willing to marry her after what she had done to him. Marry . . . ? He had not actually said he was intending to marry her but when Clare had mentioned it he made no denial. 'Do you really want to be away from Frank's grave for that long, Mrs Weedall?' Clare inquired at last.

'I'm hoping that Simon will look after it. He did promise.'

'It's a long time—and we have the busy season coming,' added Clare as the thought occurred to her. 'We might be booked up.'

A small hesitation and then, 'Perhaps, dear, if that were the case, I could share your room? Is it big enough for another bed?'

'I—I—' Clare shook her head, frowning. It would be unbearable to have Mrs Weedall with her every night. 'I never did like sharing,' she said apologetically. 'I read before going to sleep and the light would disturb you—'

'Not in the least, dear,' interrupted Mrs Weedall, smiling. 'I too read in bed so your light would be no problem.'

Clare moved uneasily. She felt she was being caught in a net from which she would have the greatest difficulty in escaping. What must she do? She could not deliberately hurt Frank's mother, and yet, if she put her first then she herself was going to be even more miserable than she was now. And the other thing was that she wanted more than anything to return to England as soon as possible. She had not yet mentioned her decision to Phil, but she had no doubt that he would be let down by her giving up the post of receptionist. Mary would readily take her place.

'I'll pay for a room if there's one available, naturally,' Mrs Weedall was saying. 'Why not see if there is one, dear, before we discuss the possibility of my sharing yours?' She looked anxiously at Clare, whose pity leapt instantly to the forefront of her mind. What a desperately

lonely woman she was! And it was not her fault
if she dwelt all the time on her misfortunes, she
just happened to be made that way, and people
like Luke and Phil should try to understand. 'I
know you have your job, Clare, dear,' continued
Mrs Weedall, 'and I know you can't be with me
during the daytime—except perhaps for lunch,'
she added on an optimistic little note. 'But there
would be every evening, and we could sit and
talk about Frank. . . .' Her voice trailed off to
silence and a tinge of colour stole into her pallid
cheeks. She and Clare were on the terrace and
Clare twisted her head to look up into the
narrowed gaze of the man who was scarcely
ever out of her thoughts.

'Luke,' she began when he interrupted her,
speaking to Mrs Weedall. 'Did I hear you say you
were staying for three months?'

'I'd like to,' answered Mrs Weedall feebly.

'And you expect Clare to spend every evening
with you?'

'She would want to be with me.'

'You're sure?' He came forward unhurriedly to
take possession of a chair opposite the woman
he was talking to. Clare noticed the steely glint
in his eyes, the harsh set of his jaw and something made her ask, 'How long have you been
there, Luke?'

'Long enough to have heard everything,' he
replied tautly.

'Yes,' Mrs Weedall was saying, 'of course I'm
sure that dear Clare would want to be with me
every evening. We've so much in common. I

expect she's told you that my son and she were engaged—and that his death left us both prostrate with grief? We only have each other—'

'Clare has parents and a brother,' broke in Luke harshly. 'While you, I believe, have a son and a daughter-in-law?'

'But they mean nothing—'

'Clare's parents are nothing to her? And Phil—?'

'Mrs Weedall doesn't mean it in that way,' interrupted Clare hurriedly. 'You've misunderstood her, Luke.'

Mrs Weedall was glancing from one to the other, a bewildered expression on her face. 'I don't understand, Mr Mortimer. It seems strange that you should interfere like this. Clare will tell you herself that she and I are united by the death of my dear son—'

'Mrs Weedall,' broke in Clare desperately, on noticing Luke's furious expression, 'Mr Mortimer isn't interested in Frank.' She turned to Luke, adding beseechingly, 'Please don't say any more. Mrs Weedall is very sad over her son's death and it isn't kind to speak to her like you are doing.'

'I don't want to be unkind, but, Mrs Weedall, your son has gone and no amount of tears or heartbreak can alter the situation. Clare has her life to live. It's five years since her fiancé died and since coming here she'd begun to get over it, but you arrived and it all began again. It's got to stop!'

'I don't understand where you come into it,'

said Mrs Weedall, gaining a little spirit from somewhere. 'You are Phil's friend, not Clare's.'

Luke and Clare exchanged glances. She was pale, troubled because of the way Luke was treating Mrs Weedall. Why had he interfered? It was not as if he had any interest in her now that Stella Wesley was here on Flamingo Cay.

'You don't know where I come into it? I shall tell you. I promised Phil that I'd try to make Clare snap out of the misery that's been affecting her for over five years.'

So that was it. The promise to Phil was the sole reason for Luke's interference. Only now did Clare realise that, for one breathless moment, she had dared to hope that there could be an altogether different reason for Luke's anger. . . .

'But you would never have succeeded,' asserted Mrs Weedall.

'That,' said Luke, 'is where you're wrong. I had almost succeeded before you arrived.'

Mrs Weedall was shaking her head. 'No, never would you make Clare forget. Why, she keeps my dear Frank's photograph beside her bed and looks at it every night. Perhaps she kisses it—we do not know, do we? It's her secret and even I would not ask her about it.'

Clare, white to the lips, had tried to interrupt but her mouth was dry; her tongue seemed paralysed.

'Is that right?' Luke turned to Clare, an incredulous expression in his eyes.

What should she do? It seemed imperative

that she tell Luke the truth—that she did *not* have Frank's photograph by her bed, nor even have a photograph of him with her. But what of Mrs Weedall? She had believed Clare when she had told the lie, saying—in order to make Mrs Weedall a little happier—that she did have a photograph of her son beside her bed. 'Well,' rasped Luke harshly, 'have you an answer to my question, Clare?'

She stared at him, unhappily aware that he would put his own interpretation on the convulsive, uncontrollable trembling of her mouth. 'Yes,' she whispered faintly at last, 'I do have Frank's photograph beside my bed.'

'My God!' Revolted, Luke got to his feet. 'You're maniacs—both of you!' And on that wrathful note he turned on his heel and left them.

'You're going home!' Phil stared at his sister uncomprehendingly. 'This is sudden, isn't it? What's happened?'

'I want to go home with Mrs Weedall.' Scalding tears pricked the backs of Clare's eyes, and her heart felt dead. To go home, back to the life which—she now knew—was a wasted one, a life controlled by the overwhelming pity she had always felt for Mrs Weedall. Clare could not help this feeling of pity; it was something stronger than herself, dominating her life, depriving her of the ability to seek for happiness.

Happiness. . . . Bitterly she knew she had come very close to real happiness, because she felt sure that, at first, Luke had a deep affection for her that could easily have strengthened to love. In fact, at one time she was convinced that he did love her, and that he was only waiting until he could be sure she had shaken off her memories before asking her to marry him. Yes, she had come so very close to happiness.

'You want to go home with Mrs Weedall?' Phil's angry voice broke into her train of thought and she looked up at him. They were in the private sitting-room of the suite which Phil, as manager of the hotel, had been given on taking up the post.

'She asked me if she could stay for three months. That was yesterday. I made up my mind definitely this morning, and when I told her she decided to come with me.' Her thoughts wandered again, to last evening when Luke and Stella had come to the Rusty Pelican for dinner and dancing.

Luke had never once cast his eyes in Clare's direction, but later, when Stella had obviously gone to the powder-room, he came over to Clare and said harshly, 'I think that, under the circumstances, you will want to be released from that work I asked you to do for me.' Clare had nodded dumbly and Luke had merely said, 'That's settled, then,' and walked away, a cold and merciless expression on his face.

Luckily Phil was not there at that particular time, so Clare was spared the questions that he would inevitably have asked.

'I suppose,' Phil was saying furiously, 'that

your first stop on landing in England will be that grave?'

'Don't be like that with me,' quivered Clare pleadingly. 'I'm n-not happy at going home, Phil, but it's the only thing I can do under the circumstances.'

He frowned then, his anger leaving him as he looked with deep concern into her ashen face.

'Clare—love, what is it? Surely you can tell me?'

'No . . . I can't tell anyone. . . .' To her great consternation she burst into tears. 'I'll—g-go to my room—'

'No, you won't!' Phil's voice was equally as authoritative as Luke's had been when he was speaking to Mrs Weedall. 'You'll stay here until I've learned what this is all about.'

She shook her head, bringing out a handkerchief and drying the tears, but only to make way for more. 'I won't tell you!' she cried, 'so you needn't ask me!'

'It's something to do with Mrs Weedall,' he persisted. 'She's been wearing you down with that same old sob story she wore you down with before, when you were at home! I'm not letting her get away with it,' he added determinedly. 'I shall go to her straight away and tell her to leave!'

'It isn't Mrs Weedall's fault,' denied Clare swiftly. 'You'll be making a mistake if you accuse her.'

'I don't believe you,' returned Phil almost brutally. 'You're my concern while you're here

—I promised Mum and Dad that I'd take good care of you. What are they to think if you go back—broken-hearted like this? I'd no right to let that woman come here—'

'Phil, please don't! You're mistaken in believing that Mrs Weedall had anything to do with my decision. She wanted to stay for three months. You know that—so how can she be the cause of my wishing to go home?'

'I'm very sure you don't *wish* to go home, Clare. You've been so settled and happy here until that woman put in an appearance!'

'I admit she's upset me at times,' returned Clare frankly, but went on to say again that Mrs Weedall had definitely not influenced her in this decision to return to England.

'She *is* the cause of your deciding to go home,' asserted Phil, ignoring her words, 'because there's no one else who could be the cause.' He was furiously angry, something most unusual for Phil. 'Why did she have to come here in the first place? And another thing,' he added as the thought crossed his mind, 'what about the work you're supposed to be doing for Luke? Are you going to let him down?'

'He'll get someone else.' Mrs Wesley . . . ? Yes, it seemed to be a foregone conclusion, decided Clare, swallowing the ache of despair that had settled in her throat.

'He's not going to be very pleased about this, Clare. You already know he was as mad as I was when he knew that Mrs Weedall was coming over here.'

'You still believe it was she who influenced me, don't you?'

'I'm sure of it—and Luke will agree with me!'

'Luke's already had his say—'

'He has?' Phil looked interrogatingly at her. 'You didn't tell me.'

'I didn't want to burden you with my troubles.'

'It's what I'm here for.'

She hesitated, but only momentarily. 'He overheard Mrs Weedall talking yesterday and didn't like what she said. And as usual he adopted that high-handed manner, almost as if he had some control over me, but this time it was directed mainly at poor Mrs Weedall; she was dreadfully upset, and when he had gone she was almost in tears.'

'It doesn't take much to bring Mrs Weedall to tears,' was Phil's disparaging comment. 'However, I'm not interested in the wretched woman's emotions,' he went on in the kind of heartless voice his sister had never before heard him use. 'What was she saying that made Luke annoyed with her?'

Clare paused, but decided it would be less fatiguing to tell Phil the whole truth, seeing that he was in this determined, almost agressive, mood. He listened without interruption, his mouth tightening as she proceeded to relate all that had taken place. 'It was just unfortunate that he overheard,' she said finally.

'This photograph?' frowned Phil shaking his head. 'You haven't a photograph of Frank with you. Mother told me in her letter that she was thankful she had been able to persuade you to leave them behind.'

Clare nodded her head. 'I did leave them behind,' she agreed, then went on to tell him the reason why she had told Mrs Weedall that she did in fact have a photograph of Frank beside her bed. 'At the time it didn't do me any harm,' she added, 'but I never thought she'd conclude that I—I kissed it every night—' She broke off, thinking of Luke's reaction and not blaming him for it. 'Luke m-must consider me—me morbid—' Again she stopped, this time to seek for a handkerchief to dry her eyes. Phil, having moved over to the window, was standing with his back to it, a most odd expression on his face.

'Why are you crying?' he asked? 'You've just said you're not happy at going home, and yet you *want* to go. It doesn't make sense. I want to know exactly what you meant by the words, "under the circumstances."'

'Don't—don't ask m-me, Phil,' she pleaded, drying her eyes and then blowing her nose hard, little realising that the action made her seem very young and vulnerable in her brother's eyes.

'There's no need for me to ask you,' he said slowly. 'You've fallen in love with Luke—'

'No! How can you say a thing like that? Would I be so—so st-stupid when it's obvious th-that he's in love with Mrs Wesley?' The handkerchief was at her eyes again but as Phil saw that it was not of much use to her he came across the room to hand her his own. His arm slipped about her and she pressed against him, seeking comfort against his chest. Sobs shook her for a few moments before she managed to regain her composure. 'I'm sorry, Phil, I should never have come here in the first place.'

He said nothing to that, merely giving a deep sigh and holding her a little more tightly against him. 'You and Luke were getting along so well at one time,' he remarked, and Clare knew by the tone of his voice that her vehement protestations had fallen on deaf ears. He knew she was in love with his friend.

'Yes, until *she* came.'

'I cannot believe he's in love with her.'

'He was once, and I daresay she's even more beautiful now than she was then.'

'Beauty!' scoffed Phil. 'What is beauty when it merely forms a veneer for a character like Mrs Wesley's? I'm very sure that Luke has some reason for paying her so much attention. She's thinking of buying one of his properties in Miami, you said?'

'Yes, but that's not the reason for his being with her so much. You've only to look at them together to see that he's attracted to her.'

'It could be the property,' murmured Phil, and now there was a strange inflection in his voice, which was very quiet, as if he were merely speaking his thoughts aloud. 'But on the other hand, it could be that his intention is to make . . .' He trailed off thoughtfully.

Clare lifted her head to regard him through eyes swollen by tears. 'What are you saying, Phil? I didn't catch it all.'

'It was nothing,' he frowned, still thoughtful and far away. Clare knew by his tone that he would not reveal what was in his mind.

'You now realise that my reason for leaving has nothing to do with Mrs Weedall? Don't you?'

Phil nodded his head. 'Yes, I do. Nevertheless, you've been made unhappy by her, Clare, and I do think you should consider making a complete break with the woman.'

'I can't, Phil. It would be too cruel. I'm the only person with whom she can talk about Frank.'

'Do you any longer want to talk about Frank—?' He stopped abruptly on hearing a quiet knock on the door. 'Come in,' he said after putting Clare from him. She turned to scan the bookshelves, her back to the waiter who had entered at her brother's invitation.

'It's Mrs Wesley,' he said, anger in his voice. 'She ordered a tray on the terrace, and because it was a little while in coming she demands to see you. We didn't keep her too long, Mr Winter, but there was this cruise ship in and we're very busy at present.'

'Don't worry about it, James. I believe we all know by now just how awkward Mrs Wesley can be. I'll come at once.'

Clare waited to hear the door close before turning around. 'How can Luke be in love with her?' she cried. 'If he marries her she'll make him so unhappy!'

'He'll never marry her,' declared Phil, a strange confidence in his voice which affected

Clare with a nebulous puzzlement that set her pulses tingling. It was almost as if Phil knew something which she did not. However, he made no further comment, merely asking her to excuse him while he dealt with Mrs Wesley's complaint.

Clare waited for a short while but when he did not come back she went out to join Mrs Weedall who was sitting in a chair beneath the shade of an hibiscus hedge.

'Ah, there you are, dear,' she greeted Clare. 'I've been thinking about your decision to go home and realise that I'm really looking forward now to being back. Can we go in about three or four days, do you think?'

'Yes, if you like,' agreed Clare without interest.

'We can then visit Frank's grave next Saturday. That'll be—'

'Mrs Weedall,' broke in Clare, a high-pitched note in her voice, the result of frayed nerves, 'please don't let us talk about Frank just now.'

'I'm sorry, Clare,' returned Mrs Weedall soothingly. 'It's too painful? I know just how you feel—the tragedy has broken both our lives, hasn't it?' Her pale eyes widened. 'You've been crying, child. But I cry myself, so very often.' Clare said nothing, and in any case her brother was coming across the lawn, a grim expression on his face.

'Was she awful?' asked Clare, mystified even yet again that Luke could like the girl.

'Worse than she's ever been. She ought to have lived when those who gave you a service were regarded as slaves! She considers everyone here as inferior!' He paused, looking down at his sister's face. 'I've just phoned Silver Springs. Luke's in Miami for a week and so I expect that's why she's in this particular mood. Perhaps she expected him to take her with him.'

'He's there on business. He'd not want Mrs Wesley.' Clare's eyes were dark and tragic, for despite the strained relationship that now existed between her and Luke, she had not thought of leaving Flamingo Cay without saying a final goodbye to him. Now, it seemed, she would never ever see him again, because once he was married to Stella Wesley there would be no question of Clare's returning to Flamingo Cay, not even for a holiday.

Mrs Weedall wasn't feeling too well that evening and asked to be excused from dinner. 'If I can have a cup of milk in my room, Clare— that'll be all I shall want.'

Clare had the milk sent up at once. She felt mean but the thought of having dinner alone with her brother seemed like a Sunday treat.

Naturally he asked about Clare's guest and seemed a trifle anxious when told she was off-colour. He and Clare were at their usual table overlooking the marina and even now, when she was feeling so unhappy, Clare was able to appreciate the attraction of a scene that had fascinated her from the first—the lights from the yachts and luxury launches, the little fishing boats bobbing about, the golden glow from the harbour itself. A crescent moon hung like a hammock, with a million stars around it, shining in a deep purple sky. In the restaurant itself there was chatter and laughter, mingling with music from the combo band. Lights were low, candles flickered; it was a romantic setting, one which Clare would never ever forget.

It was during the second course that Clare asked Phil if it would be all right if she left on the following Friday.

'Friday—this week?' he repeated with a heavy frown.

'Yes, I've already had a word with Mary and she'll be very happy to take over the desk.' Clare looked apologetically at him, a pallor on her face that was almost unhealthy, shadows in her eyes which he had not seen for a long while until today. 'I'd like to go as soon as possible, Phil, if you don't mind.'

'Luke . . . don't you want to say goodbye to him?'

'I'd have liked to, in spite of how we are with each other now, but it's obviously not to be. In any case, it would have been painful for us both, I think.'

Phil merely gave a small sigh and became thoughtful, and after a space Clare asked again if it would be all right for her to leave on Friday. 'There's a good connecting flight from Miami,' she added and at last saw him nod his head.

'Okay, if that's what you want.' He was brisk all at once, a circumstance that puzzled her greatly. 'Friday—that's in four days' time.' He was thoughtful again and presently Clare was impelled to ask, 'Have you something on your mind, Phil?'

'Plenty,' he returned and now there was a hint of amusement on his handsome face. 'If the hotel—and some of its more awkward guests— aren't enough, I have you.'

'Sorry,' she returned contritely. 'But don't worry about me, Phil. After all, I'm the one affected by all this. It was my own stupid fault, falling in love with a man who was so far above me.'

'Above?' frowned Phil questioningly. 'What gave you that idea?'

'Well, he's a millionaire for one thing, and for another he's so attractive that he could have any woman he wanted.'

'I agree with both statements, but they don't prove your point. Luke would be very annoyed if he heard you say he was above you.'

'I consider he is,' she said, a little catch in her voice.

Friday arrived at last and Clare, packing in her bedroom, marvelled at her ability to hold back the scalding tears that had gathered in a great cloud behind her eyes. Another ten or twelve hours and she would be back home . . . and her parents saddened by her arrival.

She had asked Phil to cable them and he had promised to do so. But there was something strange about him and she half-expected him to have told her before now that he had forgotten to do what she had asked. However, as he said nothing about it she concluded that the cable had been sent.

She had a suitcase on the bed and was just putting the last of her things into it when the door burst open without ceremony and, startled, she glanced up to see Luke standing there, black fury in his gaze.

'Luke! What—?' Clare's heart lurched painfully and she felt the colour drain from her face as he strode into the room, kicking the door closed behind him. 'I th-thought you were in—in Miami. Why are you here?' she asked, managing by some miracle to steady her voice, for her pulses raced madly, completely out of control. 'You've no right to come in here—'

'What the devil do you think you're doing?' he demanded wrathfully, and, without affording her an opportunity to speak, 'You're not going anywhere, so you can stop all this damned nonsense—at once!'

Dazedly Clare shook her head. 'I don't understand,' she quivered, simply because she could find nothing else to say, the only thought drifting into her consciousness the fact that Phil, troubled by her decision to leave Flamingo Cay, must have decided to phone Luke in Miami and ask his help in getting Clare to stay. And yet, Phil had appeared to be resigned, and in any case, it was not logical that Luke would take the trouble to cut short his visit to oblige his friend.

'No, because you're such an idiot! What the

hell do you mean by telling me that damned lie over the photograph?'

'I—I—Luke, what is this all about?' Filtering sunlight caught tears on her lashes and there was a catch in her voice as she added, 'Phil's been in touch obviously, but I'm still confused.'

'God, I could strangle you,' said Luke and now his voice was soft, like the sinister threat of a jungle beast. Involuntarily, Clare stepped back, her trembling fingers letting go of the scarf she was about to put in the case.

'Phil *has* been in touch with me,' he admitted. 'He's been trying for three days and managed it only a couple of hours ago. I flew over in a private plane—' He stopped, a thunderous expression in his eyes. 'Thank your lucky stars that I caught you in time, because if you'd put me to the trouble of going over to England for you I'd have given you the hiding of your life!' He stopped a moment, so that she could speak, but all she did was swallow convulsively and shake her head. It wasn't true she thought, a wild uncontrollable fluttering in the region of her heart. No, how could it possibly be true . . . ? 'And now,' he gritted, 'I suppose you *have* grasped what it's all about?'

If—you m-mean you lo—Luke, what has Phil said to you?'

Luke drew a breath as if his patience were almost exhausted. 'He told me you were in love with me, and he got in touch because it dawned on him that I might be in love with you—'

'Mrs Wesley,' quivered Clare, raising a shaky hand to her temple in a little bewildered gesture. 'What about her?'

'If you had allowed me to finish you'd have known where she came into it. Phil suspected that I was trying to make you jealous, concluding that if he was correct then obviously I *was* in love with you. So he took a chance and phoned me. I wasn't at my home or my office and so he had this difficulty—and delay.' He stopped on seeing that Clare was trying to interrupt. 'Well, what is it?' His temper was abating but Clare's happened to be rising.

'You were making me jealous!' she flashed. 'What a rotten thing to do to the girl—you—you loved! I think you're abominable!'

'No, you don't—'

'I do! You made me suffer and I hate you for it—' She got no further as Luke, covering the distance separating them in a couple of swift and agile strides, caught her in his arms and crushed her protesting body against the iron-hard muscles of his own.

'We'll soon see whether you hate me or not!' Roughly he jerked her head up; the next moment his lips were hard against hers, masterfully forcing them apart, probing the tempting depths of her mouth. For a long moment she resisted, her brain working furiously in an attempt to fill in the gaps left by Luke, to discover just how this miracle had come about. But his kisses very soon conquered her resistance and she found herself swept into reciprocal passion as his possessive hands caressed her face and throat and then found the firm contours of her breasts.

A low triumphant laugh escaped him when at last he relaxed his hold and stared down into a face flushed with happiness. 'Well,' he said, a glimmer of mockery in his smile, 'you must admit I didn't have much difficulty in overcoming the hatred you maintained you felt for me.'

Clare laughed gently and her eyes shone up into his. 'I *ought* to hate you,' she could not resist saying.

'And I ought to beat you,' was his suave yet stern rejoinder. 'What a dance you've led me! Just when I thought I'd won, and you had come to Silver Springs to tell me you loved me, it began all over again—'

'It was your fault!' she flashed indignantly. 'If you hadn't tried to make me jealous it would never have happened! And I didn't come to Silver Springs to say I loved you. Well,' she amended, 'not at first!'

'At first?'

'My reason for coming was to ask you outright if you'd any intention of going steady with that wom—er—with Mrs Wesley.'

His lips twitched at her slip but his eyes held disbelief. 'You intended asking me that?' he said.

'I suppose I'd have found a diplomatic way, of course.'

The grey eyes lit with humour. 'Even I cannot conceive of a diplomatic way in which you could have asked a question like that. However, let's not waste time on irrelevancies. If I *had* given you the answer you wanted what would you have done then?'

'If you'd told me you weren't serious about Mrs Wesley it was my intention to—to t-tell you I l-loved you. . . .' She trailed off shyly, and sent him a covert glance from beneath her lashes.

'So you did come to Silver Springs to talk about Stella?'

'Yes.'

'You told me a fib. You said you hadn't.'

Clare bypassed that, saying quickly, 'Why was she there, Luke? I mean, it wasn't an occasion when you could use her to make me jealous, was it?'

'She came uninvited. She didn't know I was using her, remember, and so she felt she'd be welcome if she called at my home.'

'Had you no qualms about using her?' asked Clare curiously.

He shook his head. 'Not at all,' he answered tightly.

'You said you'd forgiven her—that you didn't bear her a grudge.'

'I forgave her because I was indifferent and I couldn't bear her a grudge because if she hadn't thrown me over I would not have been free to marry you.' His eyes were tender as they looked down into hers, his mouth warm and strong against her quivering lips. After a little while he said ruefully, 'I think, my love, that we've both been a little foolish.'

'I know I have, and it took you to teach me that it's futile to brood, and to live on memories.'

'You don't *live* on those sort of memories, Clare, darling. But the memories we shall have—well, they'll be happy ones. I shall see to that.'

'When did you start loving me?' Clare could not help asking.

'After about a month. I didn't want to become interested in any woman—not seriously. But I must admit that even in the beginning, when you first came to Flamingo Cay, I found you attractive. So when Phil asked that favour of me it was no hardship. And after that I very soon realised that I was captivated. But at the same time I realised I had to fight a memory. You made me so angry and frustrated when you shirked the inevitable. I felt sure you loved me, and my trying to make you jealous was a last resort. It failed!' His unconscious grip on her arm made her wince. 'I felt I'd never win against that demented woman on whom you were wasting your pity!'

'*You* were sorry for her as well,' she reminded him indignantly, 'so don't blame me for the way *I* feel!'

He gave her a little shake. 'There's a limit to pity. You don't allow it to become the sole dictator of your actions.'

'I was trying hard to put the memories behind me, Luke. But when Mrs Wesley came and you gave her so much of your attention, it hurt!' There was a sudden break in her voice and a tear glistened on her lashes. 'I couldn't bear to see you with her, smiling and—'

'Dearest.' Luke's tender arms came about her and for a long moment Clare just stood close to him, her head against his breast. But after a while she looked up and said, 'It was unfortunate that you heard what Mrs Weedall was saying.'

'I was furious when I heard her say she'd like to share your room, and that she was expecting to be with you every evening. And then when she spoke of that photograph—'

'Talking of Mrs Weedall,' interrupted Clare hastily, 'she's got to be told that I'm not going home after all.' She glanced at his watch. 'We're supposed to be leaving in less than an hour. I ordered a taxi to take us to the airport.'

'There's no reason why Mrs Weedall shouldn't make use of it,' returned Luke smoothly.

'Oh, but—' Clare shook her head vigorously. 'What can I say to her, Luke? She'll be heartbroken if I don't go with her. She'll be heartbroken anyway when she learns that I'm getting married. What shall I do?'

'Tell her that you can't go back to England with her because your husband won't let you!'

'Husband. . . .' It sounded wonderful, thought Clare, her eyes glowing with love for him. But she had to say, 'You're not my husband yet, Luke.'

'I shall be in a very short time. Do you want me to come with you to see Mrs Weedall?'

'No, Luke—oh, dear,' she added, distressed, 'it'll be the worst thing I have ever done!'

'No it won't; it'll be the best thing you have ever done. Tell her that Phil will take her to the airport.'

'I must go with her,' she pleaded, looking at him with an expression that ought to have softened him but didn't. His eyes and voice were inflexible as he said, 'Phil will take her to the airport.'

'But—'

'Dear Clare,' he broke in with some asperity, 'can we forget Mrs Weedall for a moment while I kiss you?' And without giving her the chance of saying anything he bent his head and kissed her passionately on the lips. She clung to him, carried on the tide of his ardour as in her own love and longing she curved her slender body to the arching of his.

'My dear, dear love,' he whispered huskily, his lips tender on her cheek. 'When will you marry me?'

Her colour fluctuated adorably and she saw a nerve pulsating in his throat.

'Just whenever you want, Luke,' she answered shyly and, her eyes reflecting all that she felt for him, she lifted her face, inviting his kiss.

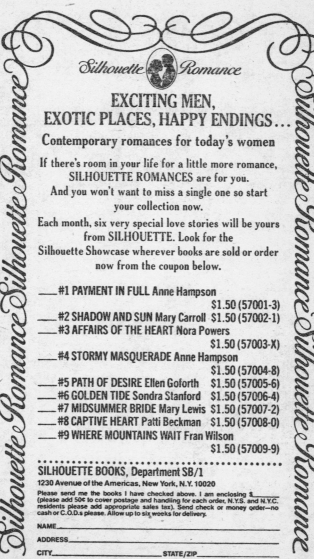